YORK NOTES

LORD OF THE FLIES

WILLIAM GOLDING

WORKBOOK BY CLARE CONSTANT

PEARSON

YORK PRESS

The right of Clare Constant to be identified as the Author of this Work has been asserted by her in accordance with the Copyright, Designs and Patents Act 1988

YORK PRESS
322 Old Brompton Road, London SW5 9JH

PEARSON EDUCATION LIMITED
Edinburgh Gate, Harlow,
Essex CM20 2JE, United Kingdom
Associated companies, branches and representatives throughout the world

First published 2015

10 9 8 7 6 5 4 3

ISBN 978–1–2921–0080–7

Illustrations by Doreen Lang; and Moreno Chiacchiera (page 48 only)

Phototypeset by DTP Media
Printed in Slovakia

Photo credits: Kichigin/Shutterstock for page 9 top / Skreidzeleu/Shutterstock for page 10 bottom / Inna Tyshchenko/Shutterstock for page 12 bottom / ULKASTUDIO/Shutterstock for page 15 top / Guschenkova/Shutterstock for page 16 bottom / abcphotosystem/Shutterstock for page 25 top / Alex Staroseltsev/ Shutterstock for page 29 top / Vitezslav Halamka/Shutterstock for page 30 bottom / Patryk Kosmider/Shutterstock for page 43 bottom / Jean-Regis Rouston/Getty Images for page 46 bottom / marekuliasz/Shutterstock for page 54 bottom / COBRASoft/Shutterstock for page 56 top

CONTENTS

PART FOUR:
THEMES, CONTEXTS AND SETTINGS

PART FIVE:
FORM, STRUCTURE AND LANGUAGE

PART SIX:
PROGRESS BOOSTER

PART ONE: GETTING STARTED

Preparing for assessment

HOW WILL I BE ASSESSED ON MY WORK ON *LORD OF THE FLIES*?

All exam boards are different but whichever course you are following, your work will be examined through these four Assessment Objectives:

Assessment Objectives	Wording	Worth thinking about ...
A01	Read, understand and respond to texts. Students should be able to: ● maintain a critical style and develop an informed personal response ● use textual references, including quotations, to support and illustrate interpretations.	● How well do I know what happens, what people say, do, etc? ● What do I think about the key ideas in the novel? ● How can I support my viewpoint in a really convincing way? ● What are the best quotations to use and when should I use them?
A02	Analyse the language, form and structure used by a writer to create meanings and effects, using relevant subject terminology where appropriate.	● What specific things does the writer 'do'? What choices has Golding made? (Why this particular word, phrase or paragraph here? Why does this event happen at this point?) ● What effects do these choices create? – Suspense? Ironic laughter? Reflective mood?
A03	Show understanding of the relationships between texts and the contexts in which they were written.	● What can I learn about society from the book? (What does it tell me about class divisions in Golding's day, for example?) ● What was society like in Golding's time? Can I see it reflected in the text?
A04	Use a range of vocabulary and sentence structures for clarity, purpose and effect, with accurate spelling and punctuation.	● How accurately and clearly do I write? ● Are there small errors of grammar, spelling and punctuation I can get rid of?

Look out for the Assessment Objective labels throughout your York Notes Workbook – these will help to focus your study and revision!

The text used in this Workbook is the Faber and Faber paperback edition, 1958.

How to use your York Notes Workbook

There are lots of ways your Workbook can support your study and revision of *Lord of the Flies*. There is no 'right' way – choose the one that suits your learning style best.

1) Alongside the York Notes Study Guide and the text	2) As a 'stand-alone' revision programme	3) As a form of mock-exam
Do you have the York Notes Study Guide for *Lord of the Flies*?	Think you know *Lord of the Flies* well?	Prefer to do all your revision in one go?
The contents of your Workbook are designed to match the sections in the Study Guide, so with the novel to hand you could:	Why not work through the Workbook systematically, either as you finish chapters, or as you study or revise certain aspects in class or at home.	You could put aside a day or two and work through the Workbook, page by page. Once you have finished, check all your answers in one go!
• read the relevant section(s) of the Study Guide and any part of the novel referred to; • complete the tasks in the same section in your Workbook.	You could make a revision diary and allocate particular sections of the Workbook to a day or week.	This will be quite a challenge, but it may be the approach you prefer.

HOW WILL THE WORKBOOK HELP YOU TEST AND CHECK YOUR KNOWLEDGE AND SKILLS?

Parts Two to **Five** offer a range of tasks and activities:

These fun and quick-to-complete tasks check your basic knowledge of the text

These more open questions challenge you to show your understanding

This task focuses in on a key character, theme, technique, idea or relationship and helps you plan and write up paragraphs for an essay

A clear, quick way to visually record your progress

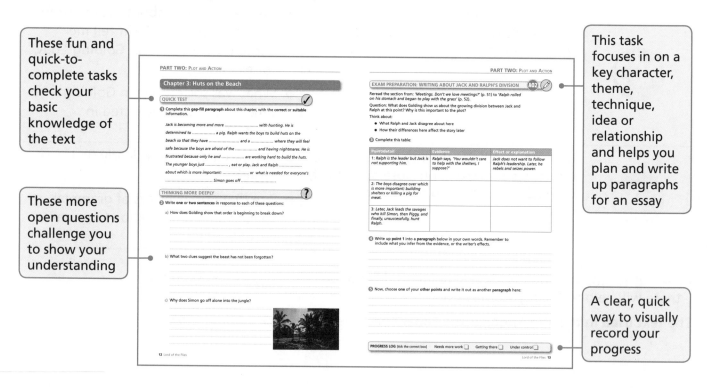

Each Part ends with a **Practice task** to extend your revision:

An exam-style task provided at end of section for you to practise a full essay

A plain table provided for you to fill in with your own ideas

The first sentence of essay provided for you to use as a prompt to start a full-length essay

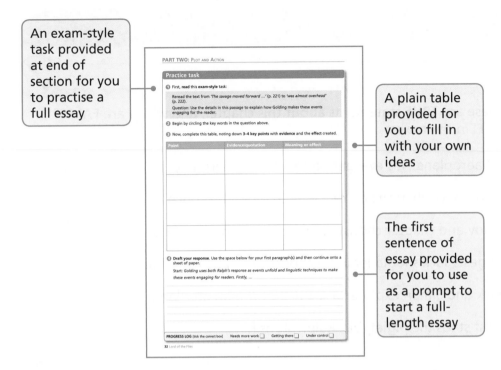

Part Six: Progress Booster helps you test your own key writing skills:

Expert teacher's or marker's view of the student's work to help you understand key skills

A sample of a student's writing challenges you to judge its strengths and weaknesses

Opportunity for you to apply what you have learned to a new point

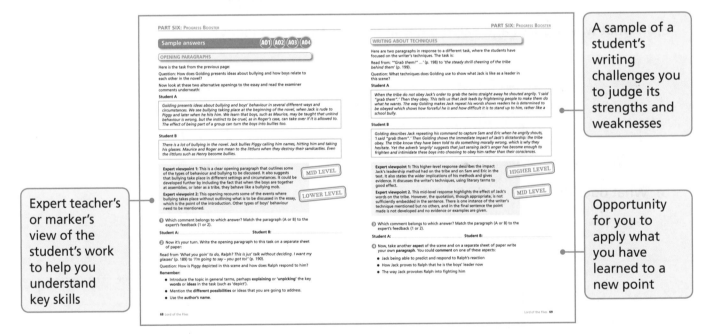

Don't forget – these are just some examples of the Workbook contents. Inside there is much, much more to help you revise. For example:

- lots of samples of students' own work at different levels
- help with spelling, punctuation and grammar
- advice and tasks on writing about context
- a full answer key so you can check your answers
- a full-length practice exam task with guidance on what to focus on

PART TWO: Plot and Action

Chapter 1: The Sound of the Shell

QUICK TEST ✔

1 Which of these are **TRUE** statements about this chapter, and which are **FALSE**? Write 'T' or 'F' in the boxes:

a) The boys' aeroplane was evacuating them from Germany. ☐

b) Piggy instructs Ralph in the correct way to blow the conch. ☐

c) As head boy and chapter chorister, Jack believes he should be 'chief'. ☐

d) Piggy suggests Jack should lead the choristers who will be hunters. ☐

e) Ralph, Jack and Simon explore to see if they are on an island. ☐

f) Jack almost stabs the piglet, but Ralph stops him. ☐

THINKING MORE DEEPLY ?

2 Write **one** or **two sentences** in response to each of these questions:

a) In what ways do Jack and Ralph differ in the way they treat Piggy?

....

....

....

....

b) What does the conch symbolise?

....

....

....

....

c) Why do you think the boys choose Ralph rather than Jack as leader?

....

....

....

....

....

EXAM PREPARATION: WRITING ABOUT THE OPENING OF THE NOVEL (A02)

Reread the beginning of the novel from *'The boy with fair hair'* (p. 1) up to *'Perhaps there aren't any grown-ups anywhere'* (p. 2).

Question: How effective is Golding's opening to the novel *Lord of the Flies*?

Think about:

- What information and ideas it reveals to readers
- How it links to the rest of the novel

3 Complete this table:

Point/detail	Evidence	Effect or explanation
1: *Ralph's and Piggy's character flaws and strengths are set up from the beginning.*	*Ralph climbs quickly and easily, ignoring the needs of Piggy, who is slow and vulnerable-looking, with 'thick spectacles'.*	*The initially unnamed main characters Golding introduces are allegorical figures who contrast with each other, suggesting they may come into conflict later.*
2: *The setting seems beautiful but threatening.*		
3: *The boys are alone and face the challenge of looking after themselves.*		

4 Write up **point 1** into a **paragraph** below in your own words. Remember to include what you infer from the evidence, or the writer's effects.

....

....

....

....

5 Now, choose **one** of your **other points** and write it out as another **paragraph** here:

....

....

....

....

....

PROGRESS LOG [tick the correct box]   Needs more work ☐   Getting there ☐   Under control ☐

Chapter 2: Fire on the Mountain

QUICK TEST ✔

1 Tick the box for the **correct** answer(s) to each of these questions:

a) What do Ralph, Jack and Simon tell the boys about the island?

there is no fresh water ☐   the fruit is poisonous ☐   it is uninhabited ☐

b) What do the boys agree about whoever holds the conch?

he can make up the rules ☐   he will not be interrupted by anyone ☐

he can only be interrupted by Ralph ☐

c) What happened to the plane that they were all on?

it was shot down in flames ☐   it is searching for them ☐   it is a mystery ☐

d) What happens to the boy with the birthmark on his face?

he drowns ☐   the beast catches him ☐   he cannot be found after the fire ☐

e) Why do the boys make a fire?

to keep warm ☐   for fun ☐   to signal to rescuers where they are ☐

THINKING MORE DEEPLY ?

2 Write **one** or **two sentences** in response to each of these questions:

a) In what ways do Ralph's and Jack's ideas about having rules differ?

....

....

....

....

b) What does the beast represent?

....

....

....

....

c) How does Ralph encourage the boys to be optimistic about being stranded?

....

....

....

....

....

....

EXAM PREPARATION: WRITING ABOUT REASON

Reread the section from *'Then when you get here you build ...'* (p. 46) to *'The crowd was a silent as death'* (p. 47).

Question: How do the details in this passage help readers understand the importance Golding places on reason in the novel?

Think about:

- What Piggy says and how the boys respond to him
- What has happened to the boy with the birthmark on his face

3 Complete this table:

Point/detail	Evidence	Effect or explanation
1: *Piggy's ability to reason and show both insight and foresight could help keep the boys safe.*	*Piggy points out the danger of fire getting out of control: 'Won't we look funny if the whole island burns up?'*	*Piggy's words are a warning and **foreshadow** the fire at the end of the novel when savagery (unreason) takes over.*
2: *Golding suggests reason needs to be combined with leadership skills.*		
3: *The disappearance of the boy with the birthmark shows the consequences of not using reason.*		

4 Write up **point 1** into a **paragraph** below in your own words. Remember to include what you infer from the evidence, or the writer's effects.

....

....

....

....

....

5 Now, choose **one** of your **other points** and write it out as another **paragraph** here:

....

....

....

....

....

....

PROGRESS LOG [tick the correct box]   Needs more work ☐   Getting there ☐   Under control ☐

Chapter 3: Huts on the Beach

QUICK TEST

❶ Complete this **gap-fill paragraph** about this chapter, with the **correct** or **suitable** information.

Jack is becoming more and more .... with hunting. He is

determined to .... a pig. Ralph wants the boys to build huts on the

beach so that they have .... and a .... where they will feel

safe because the boys are afraid of the .... and having nightmares. He is

frustrated because only he and .... are working hard to build the huts.

The younger boys just .... , eat or play. Jack and Ralph ....

about which is more important: .... or what is needed for everyone's

.... Simon goes off ....

THINKING MORE DEEPLY

❷ Write **one** or **two sentences** in response to each of these questions:

a) How does Golding show that order is beginning to break down?

....

....

....

....

....

b) What two clues suggest the beast has not been forgotten?

....

....

....

....

....

c) Why does Simon go off alone into the jungle?

....

....

....

....

....

EXAM PREPARATION: WRITING ABOUT JACK AND RALPH'S DIVISION   A02

Reread the section from: *'Meetings. Don't we love meetings?'* (p. 51) to *'Ralph rolled on his stomach and began to play with the grass'* (p. 52).

Question: What does Golding show us about the growing division between Jack and Ralph at this point? Why is this important to the plot?

Think about:

- What Ralph and Jack disagree about here
- How their differences here affect the story later

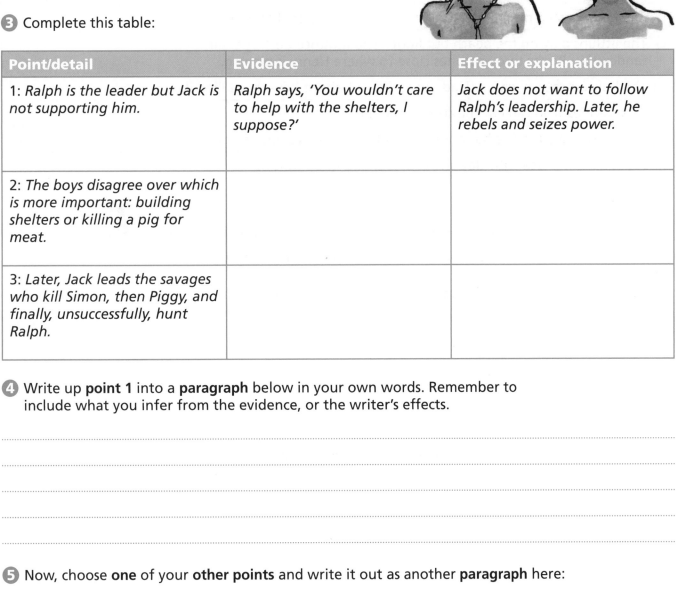

❸ Complete this table:

Point/detail	Evidence	Effect or explanation
1: *Ralph is the leader but Jack is not supporting him.*	Ralph says, 'You wouldn't care to help with the shelters, I suppose?'	Jack does not want to follow Ralph's leadership. Later, he rebels and seizes power.
2: *The boys disagree over which is more important: building shelters or killing a pig for meat.*		
3: *Later, Jack leads the savages who kill Simon, then Piggy, and finally, unsuccessfully, hunt Ralph.*		

❹ Write up **point 1** into a **paragraph** below in your own words. Remember to include what you infer from the evidence, or the writer's effects.

....

....

....

....

....

❺ Now, choose **one** of your **other points** and write it out as another **paragraph** here:

....

....

....

....

....

....

....

PROGRESS LOG [tick the correct box]   Needs more work ☐   Getting there ☐   Under control ☐

Chapter Four: Painted Faces and Long Hair

QUICK TEST

1 Number the events of this chapter so that they are in the correct sequence. Use 1 for the first event and 7 for the final event.

a) Jack hits Piggy, smashes a lens in his glasses and takes the broken glasses from Piggy without asking, in order to re-light the fire.	
b) Ralph sees a ship on the horizon, which means they could be rescued.	
c) The littluns play on the beach but Roger and Maurice destroy their sandcastles; Roger throws stones close to where Henry is playing.	
d) The hunters return with a dead pig and chant about how they killed it.	
e) Jack decides who can eat the cooked pig meat.	
f) Ralph discovers the fire has gone out and the ship sails out of sight.	
g) Jack paints his face with clay and charcoal and goes hunting.	

THINKING MORE DEEPLY

2 Write **one** or **two sentences** in response to each of these questions:

a) Which three events imply that Roger is becoming cruel?

b) What are five signs that Jack is becoming more uncivilised?

c) What is the significance of Jack taking Piggy's glasses from him?

EXAM PREPARATION: WRITING ABOUT PIGGY

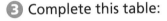

Reread the section from *'Piggy began again'* (p. 75) to *'Jus' you wait – yah'* (p. 76).

Question: With close reference to the extract, show how
Golding presents Piggy here.

Think about:

- What Piggy says and does
- How Piggy is treated by Jack and the other boys

❸ Complete this table:

Point/detail	Evidence	Effect or explanation
1: *Golding presents Piggy as the voice of authority scolding Jack for breaking his promise and letting them down.*	*Piggy says, 'You didn't ought to have let that fire go out. You said you'd keep the smoke going –'*	*Piggy does not speak with correct grammar like Jack and Ralph, but he upholds adult, civilised values such as keeping promises.*
2: *Piggy is vulnerable because Jack does not respect him. Jack hits Piggy, breaking his glasses.*		
3: *Only Simon and Ralph support Piggy by finding his glasses and criticising Jack's behaviour.*		

❹ Write up **point 1** into a **paragraph** below in your own words. Remember to
include what you infer from the evidence, or the writer's effects.

....

....

....

....

....

❺ Now, choose **one** of your **other points** and write it out as another **paragraph** here:

....

....

....

....

....

PROGRESS LOG [tick the correct box]   Needs more work ☐   Getting there ☐   Under control ☐

Chapter 5: Beast from Water

QUICK TEST ✔

1 Which of these are **TRUE** statements about this chapter, and which are **FALSE**? Write 'T' or 'F' in the boxes:

a) Ralph thinks it will be easy to persuade the boys to keep to the rules. ☐

b) The boys are risking their health and safety by breaking their basic rules. ☐

c) The beast is a giant squid with tentacles that can reach onto the island. ☐

d) Jack is confident he would be able to hunt and kill the beast. ☐

e) Jack only hates Piggy. ☐

f) Simon and Piggy agree that Ralph should step down as leader. ☐

THINKING MORE DEEPLY ?

2 Write **two** or **three** sentences in response to each of these questions:

a) What is the significance of the ellipsis (a series of dots showing where words have been left out) that ends Ralph's speech on pages 81–3?

b) What are three different reasons boys become frightened in this chapter?

c) Why is Ralph reluctant to blow the conch again at the end of the chapter?

EXAM PREPARATION: WRITING ABOUT EVIL

Reread the section from *'In a moment the platform was full of arguing, gesticulating shadows'* (p. 95) to *'What's the dirtiest thing there is?'* (p. 96).

Question: How do the details in this passage help you to understand Golding's ideas about the nature of evil in the novel? Think about:

- How the boys discuss their ideas about the beast
- The language and punctuation used

❸ Complete this table:

Point/detail	Evidence	Effect or explanation
1: *Golding suggests that evil is part of people rather than something outside them.*	*Simon is trying to explain 'mankind's essential illness'.*	*Golding suggests evil is 'essential' – a central part of humanity and 'illness' suggests evil needs curing. The novel's solutions are the pursuit of reason and choosing civilised behaviour.*
2: *Golding suggests evil makes the boys lose control and is associated with all that is uncivilised*		
3: *There are no words that can fully explain and describe what evil is like.*		

❹ Write up **point 1** into a **paragraph** below in your own words. Remember to include what you infer from the evidence, or the writer's effects.

....

....

....

....

....

❺ Now, choose **one** of your **other points** and write it out as another **paragraph** here:

....

....

....

....

....

....

PROGRESS LOG [tick the correct box]   Needs more work ☐   Getting there ☐   Under control ☐

Chapter 6: Beast from Air

QUICK TEST ✔

1 Tick the box for the **correct** answer(s) to each of these questions.

a) While the boys are sleeping, in the skies above the island

there are shooting stars ☐   war planes are fighting ☐

there is a storm ☐

b) The twins, Sam and Eric, both

see a beast which chases them ☐   are surprised by a parachute falling ☐

exaggerate when they describe the parachutist, and pretend he chased them ☐

c) The assembly agree that they want

to hide from the beast ☐   to get off the island as soon as possible ☐

the biguns to search for the beast ☐

d) The boy showing most leadership and courage while searching for the beast is:

Jack ☐   Ralph ☐   Simon ☐

THINKING MORE DEEPLY ?

2 Write **one** or **two sentences** in response to each of these questions:

a) In what ways is the adult world similar to the boys' world?

....

....

....

....

b) What is Jack's attitude towards the conch and what does this reveal?

....

....

....

....

c) How does Ralph keep his position as leader and what does this reveal?

....

....

....

....

....

EXAM PREPARATION: WRITING ABOUT LEADERSHIP

Reread the section from '*Piggy took the conch*' (p. 109) to '*So we've got to think*' (p. 110).

Question: What do we learn about the theme of leadership in this passage?

Think about:

- What the boys disagree about
- How Jack and Ralph treat the other boys

3 Complete this table:

Point/detail	Evidence	Effect or explanation
1: *Golding contrasts Jack's and Ralph's attitudes towards taking responsibility for the littluns' welfare.*	*Jack says, 'Sucks to the littluns,' whereas Ralph says, 'Someone's got to look after them.'*	*The quotations show Jack as a selfish leader, and Ralph as a caring leader. The contrast in their dialogue suggests that a good leader looks after even the weakest and most vulnerable of his followers.*
2: *Golding shows that Ralph is able to understand his own and other people's feelings, and have self control.*		
3: *Golding shows that Ralph is able to influence others to agree with him.*		

4 Write up **point 1** into a **paragraph** below in your own words. Remember to include what you infer from the evidence, or the writer's effects.

....

....

....

....

....

5 Now, choose **one** of your **other points** and write it out as another **paragraph** here:

....

....

....

....

....

....

....

PROGRESS LOG [tick the correct box]   Needs more work ☐   Getting there ☐   Under control ☐

Chapter 7: Shadows and Tall Trees

QUICK TEST ✔

1 Complete this **gap-fill paragraph** about this chapter, with the **correct** or **suitable** information.

The boys are still searching for .... Ralph notices how ....

they have all become and how much more harsh the ....

is on the other side of the island. Simon tries to reassure Ralph that he will get

.... safely. Jack discovers the tracks of a wild boar, which they

.... cruelly. The boys make up a ritual dance to celebrate the hunt

and .... gets hurt. When Ralph, Jack and Roger hunt for the beast

on the mountain, they find the dead .... and are

so terrified that they flee back down.

THINKING MORE DEEPLY ?

2 Write **one** or **two sentences** in response to each of these questions.

a) What is the effect of introducing Ralph's memories of home in this chapter?

....

....

....

....

....

b) What are two clues in the text that the boys are becoming more like savages?

....

....

....

....

....

c) Why is the tension rising between Jack and Ralph?

....

....

....

....

....

EXAM PREPARATION: WRITING ABOUT ATMOSPHERE AND MOOD   (A02)

Reread the section from *'Jack shouted'* (p. 125) to *'"Just a game," said Ralph uneasily'* (p. 126).

Question: With close reference to the text, show how Golding presents mood and atmosphere during the events described in this passage.

Think about: different techniques that are used to reveal characters' emotions.

3 Complete this table:

Point/detail	Evidence	Effect or explanation
1: *The dialogue creates an intense, frightening mood.*	*Jack takes the lead, shouting instructions to the savages circling Robert, such as 'Hold him!' and then later 'Kill him! Kill him!'*	*These short two-word instructions urge the boys to act increasingly cruelly, violently and immorally, which builds the sense of* **jeopardy** *and evil.*
2: *The chant creates a powerful, threatening atmosphere.*		
3: *The verbs in the descriptions reveal characters' strong emotions.*		

4 Write up **point 1** into a **paragraph** below in your own words. Remember to include what you infer from the evidence, or the writer's effects.

....

....

....

....

....

5 Now, choose **one** of your **other points** and write it out as another **paragraph** here:

....

....

....

....

....

....

....

PROGRESS LOG [tick the correct box]   Needs more work ☐   Getting there ☐   Under control ☐

Chapter 8: Gift for the Darkness

QUICK TEST

6 Number the events of this section so that they are in the correct sequence. Use 1 for the first event and 7 for the final event.

a)	Simon collapses after he realises that evil is part of the boys' nature, not a beast they can hunt and kill.	
b)	Ralph cannot persuade the little boys to understand the importance of the signal fire or that they could hunt for their own meat.	
c)	Piggy suggests they can build a signal fire on the beach.	
d)	Simon finds the pig's head on a stick and calls it 'Lord of the Flies'.	
e)	Jack calls a meeting and asks the boys to vote to get rid of Ralph as leader, but no one does.	
f)	Jack, dressed in a mask and with painted face, comes to steal fire and invite the rest of the boys to a feast and to join his tribe.	
g)	Jack leaves Ralph's group and establishes his own group. He leaves a pig's head as an offering to keep the beast away, and sets up a feast to persuade the other boys to join his tribe too.	

THINKING MORE DEEPLY **?**

7 Write **two** or **three sentences** in response to each of these questions.

a) Which three clues show how Piggy feels after Jack has left?

....

....

....

....

b) Why do most of the biguns decide to follow Jack?

....

....

....

....

c) What is the significance of Simon calling the pig's head 'Lord of the Flies'?

....

....

....

....

EXAM PREPARATION: WRITING ABOUT JACK

Reread the section from *'Jack turned, red in the face …'* (p. 139) to *'Ralph watched him'* (p. 140).

Question: What do the events and language in this passage reveal about Jack's character?

Think about:

- What he is trying to achieve
- How he reacts to what happens

8 Complete this table:

Point/detail	Evidence	Effect or explanation
1: *Jack is trying to take over as leader because he wants to run things in his own way and be powerful.*	Jack says, 'Who thinks Ralph oughtn't be chief?'	*Jack is not only jealous and hates Ralph: he is also arrogant, believing that he will be a better chief and that the boys will vote for him.*
2: *When Jack is rejected he feels so deeply humiliated he cannot stop himself from crying.*		
3: *Jack's response to losing face shows he is childish but also dangerous.*		

9 Write up **point 1** into a **paragraph** below in your own words. Remember to include what you infer from the evidence, or the writer's effects.

....

....

....

....

10 Now, choose **one** of your **other** points and write it out as another **paragraph** here:

....

....

....

....

....

PROGRESS LOG [tick the correct box]   Needs more work ☐   Getting there ☐   Under control ☐

Chapter 9: A View to a Death

QUICK TEST ✔

1 Which of these are **TRUE** statements about this chapter, and which are **FALSE**? Write 'T' or 'F' in the boxes:

a) Simon discovers the beast is really just a dead parachutist caught on rocks. ☐

b) Boys go to Jack's feast so they can eat meat and pretend to be a tribe. ☐

c) Piggy has brought the conch so Ralph can call an assembly. ☐

d) Jack uses reason to show that Ralph should no longer be leader. ☐

e) During the tribal dance Simon is killed because he represents the beast. ☐

f) Only the body of the dead parachutist is swept out to sea. ☐

THINKING MORE DEEPLY ?

2 Write **one** or **two sentences** in response to each of these questions:

a) How does Jack persuade boys to join his group?

....

....

....

....

b) What can you infer from this chapter about the effects of being part of a group?

....

....

....

....

....

c) What image is created during the description of Simon's body on page 170?

....

....

....

....

....

EXAM PREPARATION: WRITING ABOUT ALLEGORY

Reread the section from *'The chant rose in a tone in agony'* (p. 168) to *'bumped it over the reef and out to sea'* (p. 169).

Question: In what ways can this passage be seen as allegorical?

Think about:

- What religious ideas Simon may be used to represent
- What the hunters' actions mean in response to what Simon represents

❸ Complete this table:

Point/detail	Evidence	Effect or explanation
1: *Simon can be seen as a prophet-like figure bringing Christ's message about redemption.*	*Simon is shouting 'something about a dead man on a hill'.*	*This alludes to Christ's death and the message in the New Testament of the Bible that those who admit their evil nature and actions and want to change will be forgiven.*
2: *Golding links the hunters with people who rejected Christ and his message.*		
3: *Killing Simon represents the loss of truth and hope – then evil instincts reign.*		

❹ Write up **point 1** into a **paragraph** below in your own words. Remember to include what you infer from the evidence, or the writer's effects.

....

....

....

....

❺ Now, choose **one** of your **other points** and write it out as another **paragraph** here:

....

....

....

....

....

PROGRESS LOG [tick the correct box]   Needs more work ☐   Getting there ☐   Under control ☐

Chapter 10: The Shell and the Glasses

QUICK TEST ✓

1 Tick the box for the **correct** answer(s) to each of these questions:

a) What are the boys feeling guilty about?

They took part in the feast and dance ☐

They did not stop the savages from killing Simon ☐

They joined in with killing Simon ☐

b) How can we tell Ralph is becoming weaker?

He can't lift the logs ☐   He forgets what he wants to say ☐

He can't fight ☐

c) Which is more precious to Jack?

the conch as a symbol of authority ☐   the glasses to make fire ☐

his spear ☐

THINKING MORE DEEPLY ?

2 Write **one** or **two sentences** in response to each of these questions:

a) What clues are there in this chapter that suggest Jack acts like a cruel dictator?

....

....

....

....

b) Why can't Ralph, Piggy, Sam and Eric keep the fire alight all the time?

....

....

....

....

c) Golding was writing when many members of the Nazi Party had been put on trial for their war crimes, after the Second World War. How does the boys' response to their guilt for killing Simon reflect this context?

....

....

....

....

EXAM PREPARATION: WRITING ABOUT MORAL RESPONSIBILITY (A02)

Reread the section from *'"It was an accident," said Piggy suddenly'* (p. 173) to *'we never seen nothing'* (p. 174).

Question: How do the details and language in this passage suggest the different ways that the boys deal with the truth about Simon's murder?

Think about:

- The difference between Ralph's and Piggy's responses to what they did
- What the boys agree about at the end of the passage

❸ Complete this table:

Point/detail	Evidence	Effect or explanation
1: *At first Ralph faces up to the truth of what they did, and what it means. He is horrified and wants to be rescued.*	*Ralph says, 'I'm frightened. Of us. ... O God I want to go home.'*	*Ralph admits the truth that their evil instincts are terrifying. He is the only person in the novel to call out to God for help, and it appears that his prayer is answered.*
2: *Piggy makes excuses to avoid taking any responsibility*		
3: *The boys agree to lie to suppress the truth because they cannot bear their guilty feelings.*		

❹ Write up **point 1** into a **paragraph** below in your own words. Remember to include what you infer from the evidence, or the writer's effects.

....

....

....

....

❺ Now, choose **one** of your **other points** and write it out as another **paragraph** here:

....

....

....

....

....

PROGRESS LOG [tick the correct box]   Needs more work ☐   Getting there ☐   Under control ☐

Chapter 11: Castle Rock

QUICK TEST

❶ Complete this **gap-fill paragraph** about this chapter, with the **correct or suitable information**.

The conch group can no longer make .... and decide to

confront the .... with all their wrongdoing and demand that they

return Piggy's .... The four boys struggle to the savages'

.... on the rock. Their arguments are jeered at and Jack fights

.... Roger throws stones at Ralph and then levers a giant rock at

Piggy, smashing the conch, the symbol of .... and .... , and

killing .... Jack threatens to kill Ralph too and captures

.... and .... , leaving Ralph alone and running for his life.

THINKING MORE DEEPLY ?

❷ Write **one** or **two sentences** in response to each of these questions:

a) How does Piggy support Ralph's leadership?

....
....
....
....
....

b) When the twins 'examine Ralph' on page 192, what might they be 'noticing'?

....
....
....
....
....

c) What evidence is there that Roger is even more savage and evil than Jack?

....
....
....
....
....

EXAM PREPARATION: WRITING ABOUT LAW AND ORDER

Reread the section from *'Which is better – to have rules …'* (p. 200) to *'the body of Piggy was gone'* (p. 201).

Question: How does Golding convey the importance of law and order through the events described in this passage?

Think about: the dialogue as well as the savage boys' actions

❸ Complete this table:

Point/detail	Evidence	Effect or explanation
1: *The conch group confront the savages over the difference that divides their groups.*	*Ralph asks, 'Which is better, law and rescue, or hunting and breaking things up?'*	*This is the choice the boys, representing all humans, must make: between keeping law and order or living divisively and eventually destroying themselves.*
2: *When Roger murders Piggy it shows the terrible consequences of having no law and order.*		
3: *Golding suggests that without law and order human beings become worse than animals.*		

❹ Write up **point 1** into a **paragraph** below in your own words. Remember to include what you infer from the evidence, or the writer's effects.

....

....

....

....

....

❺ Now, choose **one** of your **other points** and write it out as another **paragraph** here:

....

....

....

....

....

....

....

PROGRESS LOG [tick the correct box]   Needs more work ☐   Getting there ☐   Under control ☐

Chapter 12: Cry of the Hunters

QUICK TEST

1 Number the events of this section so that they are in the correct sequence. Use 1 for the first event and 7 for the final event.

a) Jack and the savages track Ralph, hunting him like an animal.	
b) Ralph is frightened when he encounters the pig's head and angrily knocks away the spear that holds it up.	
c) Jack sets fire to most of the island to smoke Ralph out.	
d) Ralph finds Sam and Eric at Castle Rock. They tell him the savages' plan and that Roger has 'sharpened a stick at both ends'.	
e) Ralph collapses on the beach and sees a rescuing naval officer.	
f) As the savages feast, Ralph considers his options and tries to hide.	
g) The smoke is seen by a passing ship.	

THINKING MORE DEEPLY ?

2 Write **one** or **two sentences** in response to each of these questions:

a) What makes Ralph believe that the savages will kill him?

b) How does Golding make the hunt for Ralph tense for readers?

c) What does the naval officer represent at the end of the novel?

EXAM PREPARATION: WRITING ABOUT RALPH

Reread the section from *'I should have thought'* (p. 224) to the end of the novel.

Question: How does Golding use the details in this passage to reveal the impact living on the island has had on Ralph?

Think about:

- What Ralph says and thinks
- How the naval officer's comments contrast with Ralph's experiences

3 Complete this table:

Point/detail	Evidence	Effect or explanation
1: *The naval officer wrongly assumes that Ralph's experiences have been like those of a character in a popular adventure book.*	*The naval officer says the boys' experience was 'Like the Coral Island', but 'Ralph looked at him dumbly.'*	*'Coral Island' is an adventure story where shipwrecked boys behave in civilised and heroic ways. Ralph is silent because, in contrast, the behaviour of the boys on the island has been savage.*
2: *Ralph reflects on the deaths, destruction and evil he has experienced while on the island.*		
3: *Ralph has realised what human nature is really like, and the value of true friendship.*		

4 Write up **point 1** into a **paragraph** below in your own words. Remember to include what you infer from the evidence, or the writer's effects.

....

....

....

....

....

5 Now, choose one of your **other points** and write it out as another **paragraph** here:

....

....

....

....

....

....

PROGRESS LOG [tick the correct box]   Needs more work ☐   Getting there ☐   Under control ☐

Practice task

❶ First, **read** this **exam-style** task:

> Reread the text from *'The savage moved forward ...'* (p. 221) to *'was almost overhead'* (p. 222).
>
> Question: Use the details in this passage to explain how Golding makes these events engaging for the reader.

❷ Begin by circling the key words in the question above.

❸ Now, complete this table, noting down **3–4 key points** with **evidence** and the **effect** created.

Point	Evidence/quotation	Meaning or effect

❹ **Draft your response**. Use the space below for your first paragraph(s) and then continue onto a sheet of paper.

Start: *Golding uses both Ralph's response as events unfold and linguistic techniques to make these events engaging for readers. Firstly, ...*

....

....

....

....

....

....

PROGRESS LOG [tick the correct box]   Needs more work ☐   Getting there ☐   Under control ☐

PART THREE: CHARACTERS

Who's who?

Look at this drawing of the different characters. Without checking the novel or the York Notes Study Guide, complete the information by writing in the main **significance** of each character in the plot.

Roger

Significance: *He is a sadist who murders Piggy, tortures Sam and Eric, and plans to kill Ralph. He represents absolute savagery.*

Jack

Significance: ....

....

Ralph

Significance: ....

....

Piggy

Significance: ....

....

Maurice

Significance: ....

....

Sam and Eric

Significance: ....

....

Simon

Significance: ....

....

Ralph

1. Look at these statements about Ralph. For each one, decide whether it is **TRUE** or **FALSE**. Write 'T' or 'F' in the boxes:

   a) Ralph blows the conch to summon the other survivors. ☐

   b) Ralph organises the first fire so the boys will be warm at night. ☐

   c) Ralph makes sensible and practical rules to help the boys survive. ☐

   d) Ralph was the first to believe the beast was real. ☐

   e) Ralph is determined to remain civilised even if it costs him his life. ☐

   f) Ralph confesses to the naval officer that they murdered Simon. ☐

2. In the first column of the table below are some of Ralph's qualities. In the evidence column write a **quotation** or **detail** from the text which proves Ralph has this quality. Then **explain** what your evidence shows in terms of the novel's ideas.

Quality	Evidence	Explanation
Natural leader	*Ralph blows the conch to call together all the other survivors.*	*Ralph demonstrates good leadership skills such as taking charge and thinking of others, not just himself.*
Practical		
Sensitive to others' feelings		
Thinks about how his decisions affect others		
Courageous		

3. Read the following task:

Question: 'Ralph is the character whom Golding most approves of in the novel.' To what extent do you agree with this view?

On a separate sheet of paper, write the opening two paragraphs of a response, commenting on Ralph's most important qualities first.

Jack

1 Look at the bank of **adjectives** describing Jack. Circle the ones you think best **describe** him.

savage	playful	cheerful	arrogant	powerful
bloodthirsty	inventive	upper-class	uncivilised	aggressive
strong-willed	thoughtful	caring	cruel	moody

2 Now add a page reference from your copy of the book next to each circle showing where evidence can be found to **support** the **adjective.**

3 To what extent is Jack an **effective** leader? Sort the evidence below into **'For'** and **'Against'** by ticking the appropriate column(s). Think carefully – some evidence could prove either viewpoint.

Evidence	For	Against
a) Jack learns to hunt and provides plenty of meat for the boys.		
b) Jack does not plan ahead to ensure that everyone will stay alive and healthy, and that rescuers will be able to find them.		
c) As the story unfolds, Jack is followed by more and more of the boys and overcomes his opponents.		
d) Jack hates being led.		
e) Boys who join the savages learn to do whatever Jack wants them to.		
f) Jack encourages violence and cruelty and does not protect more vulnerable boys.		
g) Jack builds a strong sense of belonging among his followers through the face painting, chanting and feasts.		
h) Jack finds a way to manage the boys' fear of the beast.		

PROGRESS LOG [tick the correct box]   Needs more work ☐   Getting there ☐   Under control ☐

Piggy

❶ Piggy shows each of these qualities. Working from **memory**, add points in the story when they are revealed. Then find at least one quotation to prove your ideas.

Quality	Moments in the story	Quotation
Physically vulnerable		
Unpopular		
Behaves like a parent		
Source of reason and wise ideas		
Perceptive about people		
Loyal		
Lacks moral courage		

❷ Write **two sentences** explaining how Piggy's glasses are used in the novel.

....

....

....

....

❸ Using your **own judgement**, put a mark along this line to show Golding's overall presentation of Piggy:

Not at all sympathetic	A little sympathetic	Quite sympathetic	Very sympathetic
❶	❷	❸	❹

PROGRESS LOG [tick the correct box]   Needs more work ☐   Getting there ☐   Under control ☐

Simon

1 Who says? From **memory**, circle the character who makes each statement about, or to, Simon and **add the reason** it is said.

a) *'Let him alone … He's always throwing a faint … He did in Gib.; and Addis; and at matins…'* (p. 16).

Ralph   Piggy   Jack   all the boys   the beast

Why? ....

....

b) *'He might be … He's cracked'* (p. 145).

Ralph   Piggy   Jack   all the boys   the beast

Why? ....

....

c) *'we shall do you. See? Jack and Roger and Maurice and Robert and Bill and Piggy and Ralph. Do you. See?'* (p. 159).

Ralph   Piggy   Jack   all the boys   the beast

Why? ....

....

d) *'Kill the beast! Cut his throat! Spill his blood! Do him in!'* (p. 168).

Ralph   Piggy   Jack   all the boys   the beast

Why? ....

....

e) *'he had no business crawling like that out of the dark. He was batty. He asked for it … It was an accident'* (p. 173).

Ralph   Piggy   Jack   all the boys   the beast

Why? ....

....

2 Simon's understanding of what the beast represents grows during the course of the novel. Complete these quotations which describe the beast and human nature.

a) *'However Simon thought of the .... , there rose before his inward*

sight the picture of a human at once .... and

.. ' (p. 112).

b) *'I'm .... of you? Close, close, ... I'm the .... why it's*

no go? Why .... are what they are?' (p. 158).

Roger

❶ Complete this **gap-fill paragraph** about Roger, adding the **correct information** or **quotation** using the page references to help you:

Roger enjoys ……………………… others because he is a sadist, which makes him more evil than Jack. In Chapter 1 we learn that he 'kept to himself with ……………………… and ……………………….' (p. 18). Under Jack's lawless leadership, he unleashes his natural ………………… . Firstly, he throws ………………… at an unsuspecting littlun, ………………… , so that they miss him, but only because he still feels as if ………………… is under the protection of ………………… and ……………………… and ……………………… and the ……………………… (p. 65). Later, Roger deliberately kills ……………………………… with a boulder and feels 'a sense of delirious ………………………………….' (p. 200). Roger's role in Jack's group is to be the ……………………………… , and the twins tell Ralph that Roger is a ……………………………… (p. 210) whom they are afraid of. They warn him that Roger has sharpened the stick at both ……………………………… (p. 211), suggesting that he intends to ……………………… Ralph's head as an ……………………… to the beast.

Maurice

❶ Decide how **similar** Maurice is to Roger by ticking the **'Similar'** or **'Different'** column in the table below. Think carefully: you may decide you need to tick both columns.

Maurice's qualities and actions	Similar to Roger	Different from Roger
a) Maurice is a follower.		
b) Maurice breaks up the littluns' sandcastles (p. 62).		
c) Maurice is 'most at home' on the island (p. 68).		
d) Sometimes Maurice finds ways to calm things down (p. 79).		
e) Maurice adds to the boys' belief that the beast is real (p. 95).		
f) Maurice is afraid of the beast (p. 178).		

PROGRESS LOG [tick the correct box]   Needs more work ☐   Getting there ☐   Under control ☐

Sam and Eric

1 Look at these statements about the twins Sam and Eric. For each one, decide whether it is **True** or **False**. Write 'T' or 'F' in the boxes:

a) The twins help Simon and Ralph build the huts on the beach. ☐

b) The twins remain loyal to Ralph until they are captured by the savages. ☐

c) The twins' separate identities becomes blurred because they look and behave so similarly and are usually together. ☐

d) The twins discover the dead parachutist and decide to pretend he is the beast. ☐

e) The twins say they saw how Simon was killed. ☐

f) The twins are terrified of Roger and Jack and so they join the savages. ☐

2 **Complete** these **statements** about Sam and Eric:

a) We can tell the twins feel guilty about their part in Simon's murder because

....

b) The twins represent people who are forced to do evil by their leaders because

....

c) When the Ralph finds the twins on duty they still try to help him by

....

3 Write **two sentences** saying what you think Sam and Eric contribute to the novel:

....
....
....
....
....
....
....

4 Using your **own judgement**, put a mark along the line to show how civilised the twins are during the novel.

Not at all civilised	A little civilised	Quite civilised	Very civilised
①	②	③	④

PROGRESS LOG [tick the correct box]   Needs more work ☐   Getting there ☐   Under control ☐

Minor characters

1 From **memory**, make a list of the littluns' names, then **check** to see if you have

recalled them all: ....

....

2 Complete these statements about the littluns.

a) The little boy with a 'mulberry birthmark' says he saw the beastie, which ....

....

After the fire he has disappeared, suggesting he is the first boy to ....

....

b) At first Percival is always able to recite his ....

By the end of the novel when he meets the naval officer, he cannot remember it, which suggests

that ....

c) Robert imitates the pig being .... , which foreshadows the death of

and also the final hunt for ....

d) The littluns are often shown as a group who ....

but by the end of the novel have become ....

....

....

3 Complete this **gap-fill paragraph** about the **dead parachutist**:

The dead parachutist arrives on the island because his plane has been ....

His rotting body is found on three occasions: firstly by .... ,

who fear he must be the .... , an idea confirmed when ....

investigates. Later, Simon realises the .... but is killed before he can explain.

A .... sweeps the dead parachutist's body out to ....

4 Answer this question: how does **the naval officer** expect the boys to have behaved

while stranded on the island?

....

....

....

....

....

| PROGRESS LOG [tick the correct box] | Needs more work ☐ | Getting there ☐ | Under control ☐ |

Practice task

1 First **read** this **exam-style** task:

> Reread the text from *'Simon's head was tilted slightly ...'* (p. 158) to *'fell down and lost consciousness'* (p. 159).
>
> Question: Beginning with the details in this extract, to what extent is the beast an important character in the novel?

2 Begin by circling the **key words** in the **question** above.

3 Now, complete this table, noting down **3–4 key points** with **evidence** and the **effect** created.

Point	Evidence/quotation	Meaning or effect

4 **Draft your response**. Use the space below for your first paragraph(s) and then continue onto a sheet of paper.

Start: *The beast is important because the boys have different ideas about what it is and how to deal with it ...*

....

....

....

....

....

....

....

PROGRESS LOG [tick the correct box]   Needs more work ☐   Getting there ☐   Under control ☐

PART FOUR: THEMES, CONTEXTS AND SETTINGS

Themes

1 Things breaking down is a central theme in *Lord of the Flies*. Make a **note** of how each of these things changes for the worse in the novel and add **one** or **two examples**:

a) *Friends become enemies, e.g. Ralph and Jack.*

b) Technology *becomes* ....

   Example(s): ....

c) Law and order *turn to* ....

   Example(s): ....

d) Clothes *become* ....

   Example(s): ....

e) Peace *becomes* ....

   Example(s): ....

f) The beautiful tropical island *becomes* ....

   Example(s): ....

g) Life *turns into* ....

   Example(s): ....

2 **Circle** the themes below which are **most relevant to** the novel:

age	war	violence	law and order
fear	human nature	power	love	civilisation
Britishness	reason	time	education

3 Write down any **further themes** you think the novel explores below:

....

....

....

....

....

....

....

PROGRESS LOG [tick the correct box]   Needs more work ☐   Getting there ☐   Under control ☐

THINKING MORE DEEPLY

4 Write **three sentences** explaining what the novel reveals about these themes:

Human nature

Golding shows that people are ....

....

....

....

....

Civilisation

Golding suggests that civilisation is ....

....

....

....

....

5 Choose the **two themes** you think are most important in the novel and explain your reasons in your own words.

Theme 1. *I think the most important theme is* ....

because ....

....

....

....

....

....

Theme 2. *I think the second most important the theme is* ....

because ....

....

....

....

....

6 It is important that you use **quotations** to explain **themes**. Read this quotation from Ralph and then:

- Write down what theme(s) it represents
- Add further comments to explain what it reveals, or make links

'… you're breaking the rules!'

'Who cares?'

Ralph summoned his wits. 'Because the rules are all we have got.' **(p. 99)**

'wits' suggests that the ability to reason is why people are civilised

7 Many of the **events** and **symbols** in the novel link to **themes** very strongly. What themes do these events or symbols link to?

a) Roger throwing stones near Henry and deliberately missing him

Links to the theme of ....

Why? ....

....

b) Ralph going ahead to climb to the top of the mountain to see if the beast is there

Links to the theme of ....

Why? ....

....

c) Simon talking to the pig's head as if it is the Lord of the Flies

Links to the theme of ....

Why? ....

....

d) The symbol of Piggy's glasses

Links to the theme of ....

Why? ....

....

e) The symbol of the conch

Links to the theme of ....

Why? ....

....

PROGRESS LOG [tick the correct box] Needs more work ☐ Getting there ☐ Under control ☐

EXAM PREPARATION: WRITING ABOUT SAVAGERY

Reread the section from '*Here, struck down by the heat …*' (p. 148) to '*boys cried with laughter*' (p. 149).

Question: What do the details in this passage reveal about the theme of savagery?

Think about:

- Roger's and Jack's behaviour
- How the other boys respond to killing the pig

8 Complete this table:

Point/detail	Evidence	Effect or explanation
1: *Golding suggests that savagery is frightening and unnatural.*	'*This dreadful eruption from an unknown world made her frantic …*'	*The pig is an animal but is not used to savage behaviour, suggesting that this behaviour does not occur in nature but only in humans.*
2: *Savagery is cruel and causes great and unnecessary suffering.*		
3: *It can become normal behaviour to those who accept it.*		

9 Write up **point 1** into a **paragraph** below in your own words. Remember to include what you infer from the evidence, or the writer's effects:

....

....

....

....

10 Now, choose **one** of your **other points** and write it out as another **paragraph** here:

....

....

....

....

....

....

PROGRESS LOG [tick the correct box]   Needs more work ☐   Getting there ☐   Under control ☐

Contexts

QUICK TEST ✔

1 Tick the box for the **correct** answer to each of these questions:

a) During Golding's childhood the following book was popular and influenced his writing of *Lord of the Flies*:

The Lion, The Witch and The Wardrobe ☐   *Mein Kampf* ☐   *Coral Island* ☐

b) Lord of the Flies was written in 1954, when people were afraid of:

the Second World War ☐   a nuclear war happening ☐

the Loch Ness Monster ☐

c) Golding had seen the terrible consequences of which form of government?

dictatorship ☐   theocracy ☐   democracy ☐

d) Golding taught boys in public schools, which led him to believe that without the influence of education and discipline human nature was basically:

selfish ☐   good ☐   savage ☐

e) Golding was interested by Freud's psychological theory that the human mind was a battle ground between:

memories, emotions and greed ☐   instincts, reasoning and morality ☐

imagination and supernatural influences ☐

THINKING MORE DEEPLY ?

2 Write **two** or **three sentences** in response to each of these questions:

a) How does *Lord of the Flies* reflect Golding's ideas about humans' responsibility for the atrocities carried out during the Second World War?

....

....

....

....

b) Golding was a Christian. How does this religious belief shape the novel?

....

....

....

....

....

....

EXAM PREPARATION: WRITING ABOUT CONTEXTS

Question: Jack is presented as a public school boy. To what extent does he reflect Golding's ideas about what boys of his time were really like?

Remember to refer to events in the novel as well as its social, cultural and historical context.

❸ Complete this table:

Point/detail	Evidence	Effect or explanation
1: *Jack is head boy of his school, which makes him arrogant and think that he is entitled to lead.*	*' "I ought to be chief," said Jack with simple arrogance, "because I'm chapter chorister and head boy. I can sing C sharp." ' (p. 18)*	*We can see the hierarchy and class divisions of 1950s society reflected in the behaviour of boys such as Jack.*
2: *Jack shows contempt for people who do not share his upbringing.*		
3: *Jack rapidly descends into savagery.*		

❹ Write up **point 1** into a **paragraph** below in your own words. Remember to include what you infer from the evidence, or the writer's effects:

....
....
....
....
....

❺ Now, choose **one** of your **other points** and write it out as another **paragraph** here:

....
....
....
....
....
....
....

PROGRESS LOG [tick the correct box]   Needs more work ☐   Getting there ☐   Under control ☐

Settings

❶ Underneath the name of each key location below write the significant event(s) that take place there.

Location: The mountain top

Event(s): ....

Location: Castle Rock

Event(s): ....

....

Location: The huts

Event(s): ....

....

Location: The pool

Event(s): ....

....

Location: The platform

Event(s): ....

....

THINKING MORE DEEPLY

2 Write **two** or **three sentences** in response to each of these questions:

a) How suitable is the Castle Rock as a base for the boys to live on?

....

....

....

....

....

b) What can you infer about Jack's leadership from his choice of Castle Rock as a base ?

....

....

....

....

....

c) Reread page 49. How is the description of the jungle used to imply ideas about Jack's nature?

....

....

....

....

....

....

....

....

d) Read the description of the sea on pages 120–1 and explain its effect on Ralph.

....

....

....

....

....

....

....

....

PROGRESS LOG [tick the correct box]   Needs more work ☐   Getting there ☐   Under control ☐

Practice task

1 First read this exam-style task:

> Reread the text from *'Towards midnight ...'* (p. 169) to *'towards the open sea'* (p. 170).
>
> Question: How do the details Golding uses in this setting suggest the significance of Simon's role in the novel?

2 Begin by circling the key words in the question above.

3 Now, complete this table, noting down **three** or **four key points** with **evidence** and the **effect** created.

Point	Evidence/quotation	Meaning or effect

4 Draft your response. Use the space below for your first paragraph(s) and then continue onto a sheet of paper.

Start: *Golding's use of light in the description suggests ...* ....

....

....

....

....

....

....

....

....

....

....

PROGRESS LOG [tick the correct box]   Needs more work ☐   Getting there ☐   Under control ☐

PART FIVE: FORM, STRUCTURE AND LANGUAGE

Form

QUICK TEST ✓

1 Complete this **gap-fill paragraph** explaining the form in which the novel is written:

'Lord of the Flies' is a dystopian novel which draws on several genres. Firstly,

it is a boys' .... story, like 'Coral Island', with boys stranded

on a desert island.

However, it also alludes to the boarding school stories popular in the early

.... century. Golding drew on the comic figure of

Billy Bunter in the characterisation of .... , who is

.... , wears .... and is a figure of fun.

The novel also works as an allegory, with characters representing

.... and the story conveying the message that without

.... savagery takes over.

THINKING MORE DEEPLY ?

2 Many characters in the novel are **allegorical**. They **represent ideas**. Write one or two sentences explaining what ideas each of these characters represents:

Simon represents ....

....

....

Ralph represents ....

....

....

Piggy represents ....

....

....

....

Jack represents ....

....

....

....

PROGRESS LOG [tick the correct box]   Needs more work ☐   Getting there ☐   Under control ☐

Structure

1 The story is told in chronological (time) order. Put these events in the order in which they happen in the text. Number the events below 1 to 6 (1 for the first event; 6 for the last event).

Event	Order
a) All but a few boys join the savages who steal Piggy's glasses. Piggy is killed, the conch is destroyed, and Sam and Eric are captured, leaving Ralph alone.	
b) Fear of the beast grows and so does the conflict between Jack and Ralph. The dead parachutist's body is mistaken for the beast.	
c) The savages hunt Ralph, intending to kill him, and start a fire to smoke him out. The smoke is seen by a ship and a naval officer arrives in time to save Ralph.	
d) Jack leaves Ralph's group and forms the savage tribe, who kill a sow, offer its head to the beast and hold a feast at which Simon is killed.	
e) Ralph tries to build huts and organise the boys, but Jack becomes so obsessed with hunting that the signal fire goes out and they miss the chance to be rescued.	
f) Ralph blows the conch to call an assembly and he, Jack and Simon explore to discover whether they are on an island. Later they make the signal fire but let it burn out of control.	

2 There are lots of clues which **foreshadow** later events in the novel. What event does each of these clues foreshadow?

a) The rolling of the boulders off the Castle Rock on (p. 117) foreshadows

....

....

b) Maurice acting out the pig being hunted by the savages (p. 149) foreshadows

....

....

c) The Lord of the Flies warns Simon 'We are going to have fun' and lists the boys

who will 'do you' (pp. 158–9). This foreshadows ....

....

....

....

PROGRESS LOG [tick the correct box]   Needs more work ☐   Getting there ☐   Under control ☐

EXAM PREPARATION: WRITING ABOUT STRUCTURE

Question: How does the way Golding structures the novel create suspense for readers?

Think about:

- The order of events
- His use of techniques such as *foreshadowing*

③ Complete this table:

Point/detail	Evidence	Effect or explanation
1: *Telling the events in chronological order enables the story to build to a climax.*	*Readers see the deterioration of the relationship between Ralph and Jack, and Jack's increasing savagery.*	*By the end, we have seen the savages' murders of Simon and Piggy, and expect Ralph to be their third victim.*
2: *Golding's* **foreshadowing** *of what may come next creates a sense of threat and menace.*		
3: *Golding creates a sense of* **jeopardy** *as the hunters get closer and closer to Ralph, and the fire means that he cannot escape.*		

④ Write up **point 1** into a **paragraph** below in your own words. Remember to include what you **infer** from the **evidence**, or the writer's **effects**:

....

....

....

....

....

⑤ Now, choose **one** of your **other points** and write it out as another **paragraph** here:

....

....

....

....

....

....

....

PROGRESS LOG [tick the correct box]   Needs more work ☐   Getting there ☐   Under control ☐

Language

QUICK TEST

1 **Name** the literary techniques used in each of the following quotations:

a) 'the silvery laughter scattered' (p. 198) ....

b) 'a faint "Zup!"' (p. 199) ....

c) 'vivid stars were spilt and danced all ways' (p. 208) ....

d) 'Heave! Heave! Heave!' (p. 214) ....

e) 'two boys, bullet-headed' (p. 14) ....

THINKING MORE DEEPLY

2 Golding's choice of vocabulary implies information about characters. Write **two** or **three sentences** in response to the questions below.

a) Read page 8. How is the class difference between Piggy and Ralph implied in the different ways in which they speak?

....

....

....

....

....

....

....

....

b) How are you able to infer Jack's public school upbringing from the language he uses to explain Simon's faint on page 16?

....

....

....

....

....

....

....

....

3 Golding juxtaposes Latinate and Anglo-Saxon vocabulary to highlight the difference between civilisation and savagery. Describe how this idea is present in this quotation from page 209:

'Eric took up; and then the twins started their antiphonal speech.'

....

....

....

....

4 When you notice a writer using a technique, it is important to understand what effect it has on readers. Think about the technique used in these quotations, and explain what effect it has and how it helps to convey the writer's intention.

    a) Punctuation e.g. of Sam and Eric's speech on page 209:

        '– they made us –'

        '– we couldn't help it –'

Explain the technique and how it is used in the quotation: ....

....

....

What effect does it have? ....

....

How does this help convey the writer's intention? ....

....

....

....

    b) Synecdoche e.g. 'Below him, Ralph was a shock of hair and Piggy a bag of fat' (p. 199).

Explain the technique and how it is used in the quotation: ....

....

....

What effect does it have? ....

....

....

How does this help convey the writer's intention? ....

....

....

....

....

| PROGRESS LOG [tick the correct box] | Needs more work ☐ | Getting there ☐ | Under control ☐ |

Reread the section from '*He wormed his way…*' (p. 216) to '*If only one had time to think!*' (p. 217).

Question: How does Golding use language in this passage to imply Ralph's fear and the desperation of his situation?

Think about:

● Vocabulary choices

● Literary techniques

5 Complete this table

Point/detail	Evidence	Effect or explanation
1: *Ralph is compared to animals as he is hunted.*	'*He wormed his way …*' '*… like a cat …*'	*In these similes Ralph is compared to small animals. Readers know how brutally the savages kill pigs, larger than cats or worms, so Ralph does not seem to stand a chance.*
2: *Ralph cannot recognise the boys individually; they all appear to be savages.*		
3: *Ralph speaks to himself in formal, civilised language.*		

6 Write up **point 1** into a **paragraph** below in your own words. Remember to include what you infer from the evidence, or the writer's effects:

....

....

....

....

7 Now, choose **one** of your **other points** and write it out as another **paragraph** here:

....

....

....

....

....

PROGRESS LOG [tick the correct box]   Needs more work ☐   Getting there ☐   Under control ☐

Practice task

1 First read this exam-style task:

Question: Explain how Golding uses language to help him convey the conflict between Jack and Ralph in the novel.

2 Begin by circling the **key words** in the question above.

3 Now, complete this table, noting down **three** or **four key points** with **evidence** and the **effect** created.

Point	Evidence/quotation	Meaning or effect

4 Draft your response. Use the space below for your first paragraph(s) and then continue onto a sheet of paper.

Start: *As the novel progresses, Golding uses the way Jack and Ralph speak to convey ...*

....

....

....

....

....

....

....

....

....

....

PROGRESS LOG [tick the correct box]   Needs more work ☐   Getting there ☐   Under control ☐

PART SIX: Progress Booster

Writing skills

1 How well can you express your ideas about *Lord of the Flies*? Look at this grid and tick the level you think you are currently at:

Level	How you respond	What your spelling, punctuation and grammar are like	Tick
Higher	• You analyse the effect of specific words and phrases very closely (i.e. 'zooming in' on them and exploring their meaning). • You select quotations very carefully and you embed them fluently in your sentences. • You are persuasive and convincing in the points you make, often coming up with original ideas.	You use a wide range of specialist terms (words like 'imagery'), excellent punctuation, accurate spelling, grammar, etc.	
Mid	• You analyse some parts of the text closely, but not all the time. • You support what you say with evidence and quotations, but sometimes your writing could be more fluent to read. • You make relevant comments on the text.	You use a good range of specialist terms, generally accurate punctuation, usually accurate spelling, grammar, etc.	
Lower	• You comment on some words and phrases but often you do not develop your ideas. • You sometimes use quotations to back up what you say but they are not always well chosen. • You mention the effect of certain words and phrases but these are not always relevant to the task.	You do not have a very wide range of specialist terms, but you have reasonably accurate spelling, punctuation and grammar.	

SELECTING AND USING QUOTATIONS

2 Read these two samples from students' responses to a question about how Jack is presented. Decide which of the three levels they fit best, i.e. **lower** (L), **mid** (M) or **higher** (H).

Student A: *Jack tells Ralph he should be the boys' leader, because he is 'chapter chorister and head boy', which tells us he has been a leader before. He also says he can sing 'C sharp', which is very high. We can see Jack is proud of his achievements.*

Level? ☐ Why?

....

Student B: *Jack is too proud to be led by Ralph so he explains with 'simple arrogance' why he should be leader. Jack's reasons for thinking he should be leader, 'because I'm chapter chorister and head boy', have nothing to do with how well he can help the boys survive on the island, as the noun 'arrogance' indicates. Jack feels entitled to be the leader just because he has been one at school.*

Level? ☐ Why?

....

ZOOMING IN – YOUR TURN!

Here is the first part of another student response. The student has picked a good quotation but he hasn't 'zoomed in' on any particular words or phrases:

> When Jack proudly tells Ralph he has cut the pig's throat, Golding tells us 'yet he twitched as he said it', implying that the memory is uncomfortable.

③ Think carefully about **words** or **phrases** the student has quoted and write a further sentence to complete the explanation:

The word/phrase '..' suggests that ....

....

....

EXPLAINING IDEAS

You need to be precise about the way Golding gets ideas across. This can be done by varying your use of verbs (not just using 'says' or 'means').

④ Read this paragraph from a **mid-level** response to a question about Jack's relationship with Piggy. Circle all the **verbs** that are repeated in the student's writing (not in the quotations):

> After he lets the signal fire go out Golding shows how Jack's pride affects him when he hits Piggy in the stomach and says 'You would, would you Fatty?' It says that rather than admit he has done something wrong, Jack bullies Piggy, who is weaker than him and unlikely to hit him back. Calling him 'Fatty' says Jack wants to humiliate Piggy. Through Jack's question, Golding says that Jack is pretending to defend himself, when really he is bullying Piggy.

⑤ Now choose some of the words below to replace your circled ones:

suggests	implies	tells us	presents	signals	asks
demonstrates	recognises	comprehends	reveals	conveys	

⑥ Rewrite your **higher-level** version of the paragraph in full below. Remember to mention the **author by name** to show you understand he is **making choices** in how he presents characters, themes and events.

....

....

....

....

....

....

....

....

PROGRESS LOG [tick the correct box]   Needs more work ☐   Getting there ☐   Under control ☐

Making inferences and interpretations

WRITING ABOUT INFERENCES

You need to be able to show you can read between the lines, and make inferences, rather than just explain more explicit 'surface' meanings.

Here is an extract from one student's **very good** response to a question about Piggy and the way he is presented:

> *During the assembly when the boys discuss the beast, Piggy shows contempt for the idea that it could be a ghost, asking, 'What are we? Humans? Or animals? Or savages?' He thinks that humans are rational and should not believe in things like ghosts. His questions also suggest that he thinks humans are a higher form of life, an improvement on both animals and the savages he believes were their ancestors. However, through the novel Golding demonstrates Piggy's error: inside every civilised human being is a savage.*

1 Look at the response carefully.

- **Underline** the simple point which explains what Piggy does.
- **Circle** the sentence that develops the first point.
- **Highlight** the sentence that shows an inference and begins to explore wider interpretations.

INTERPRETING – YOUR TURN!

2 Read the opening to this student response carefully and then **choose the sentence** from the list which shows **inference** and could lead to **a deeper interpretation**. Remember – interpreting is *not* guesswork!

> *When Jack tries to speak without the conch Ralph shows he believes keeping the rules they have agreed is important when he says: 'the rules are the only thing we've got'. This shows that he thinks the boys lost a lot in the plane crash, but they still know how to behave. It also suggests that …*

a) *the rules will keep the boys safe from the beast and help them get rescued.*

b) *without the rules the boys will lose any sense of order and civilisation and everything will fall apart – they will become savages.*

c) *the boys don't have any photographs of their families or other mementos to remind them of home.*

3 Now complete this **paragraph** about Roger, adding your own final sentence which makes inferences or explores wider interpretations:

> *Roger is presented by Golding as the cruellest, and least civilised character. At the end of the novel he kills Piggy with a boulder and feels only 'delirious abandonment'. This suggests that …* ....

....

....

....

PROGRESS LOG [tick the correct box]   Needs more work ☐   Getting there ☐   Under control ☐

Writing about context

EXPLAINING CONTEXT

When you write about context you must make sure that what you write is relevant to the task.

Read this comment by a student about the naval officer:

The mistaken ideas of the naval officer, an adult, about how boys would behave while left alone on the island is expressed in his statement 'Like the Coral Island'. He is referring to a popular Victorian children's novel which described three British boys stranded on an island living happily together defeating visiting foes such as pirates, savages, etc. Golding makes Ralph 'dumb' in response to the naval officer's suggestion to emphasise how wrong this view of humanity was.

1 Why is this an effective paragraph about context? Select a), b) or c).

   a) Because it explains what the novel *Coral Island* was about, how exciting a book it is and how he is reminded of the fun and excitement of being a child stranded on a tropical island.

   b) Because it makes the link between the unrealistic ideas about human nature in *Coral Island* and Golding's views in *Lord of the Flies*, and shows how they contrast.

   c) Because it explains that the naval officer has no idea what Ralph has experienced.

YOUR TURN!

2 Now read this further paragraph, and complete it by choosing a suitable point related to context, selecting from a), b) or c) below.

Golding shows that the boys' descent into savagery cannot be dismissed as being due to their age or immaturity when he describes the dead parachutist's arrival: 'a sign came down from the world of grown ups'.

   a) *The parachutist symbolises the atrocities adults committed during the Second World War, shortly before the book was written, and reminds readers that supposedly mature adults behaved far more savagely than the boys.*

   b) *The parachutist reminds readers that the boys are at least protected from the world's problems while they live on the island. No bombs land on them and no enemy forces arrive and capture them. Instead, they have plenty to eat and drink.*

   c) *The parachutist symbolises the fact that unexpected events happen and you have to get on with life and make the most of it whether you are young or old. None of us knows when we are going to die, just like Piggy and Simon did not expect to die at a young age.*

3 Now, on a separate sheet of paper, write a paragraph about how Golding uses the context of the Billy Bunter stories, and common attitudes in the 1950s towards bullying, in his portrayal of Piggy.

PROGRESS LOG [tick the correct box]   Needs more work ☐   Getting there ☐   Under control ☐

Structure and linking of paragraphs

Paragraphs need to demonstrate your points clearly by:

- using topic sentences
- focusing on key words from quotations
- explaining their effect or meaning

1 Read this paragraph in which a student explains how Golding presents Simon:

Golding presents Simon as a spiritual character. He brings a message about the true nature of the evil the boys fear when he shouts 'something about a dead man on a hill'. The words 'dead man on a hill' are an allusion to Christ's death, and in the words of Simon's message Golding links the boys' experience to the Christian view that humans are responsible for their choice to do evil and only God can help them overcome this impulse.

Look at the response carefully.

- **Underline** the topic sentence which explains the main point about Simon.
- **Circle** the words that are picked out from the quotation.
- **Highlight** or put a tick next to the part of the last sentence which explains the word.

2 Now read this **paragraph** by a student who is explaining how Golding presents Maurice:

We find out about Maurice when he 'still felt the unease of wrongdoing' after kicking the littluns' sandcastles. This tells us he feels uncomfortable because he knows it was wrong.

Expert viewpoint: This paragraph is unclear. It does not begin with a topic sentence to explain how Golding presents Maurice and doesn't zoom in on any key words that tell us what Maurice is like.

Now **rewrite the paragraph**. Start with a **topic sentence**, and pick out a **key word or phrase** to **'zoom in'** on, then follow up with an explanation or interpretation.

Golding presents Maurice as ... .

....

....

....

....

....

....

....

....

....

It is equally important to make your sentences link together and your ideas follow on fluently from each other. You can do this by:

- using a mixture of short and long sentences as appropriate
- using words or phrases that help connect or develop ideas

❸ Read this paragraph by one student writing about Jack and how he is presented:

> *Golding presents Jack as a highly civilised boy who descends into savagery over the course of the novel. Initially, Jack appears fully dressed in his choir school uniform, which suggests that he is a model public school boy, and boasts that he is 'chapter chorister and head boy', implying that he is highly civilised. The inference is that he should make an ideal leader. Later, however, he is a changed person. Almost naked and daubed with paint, after declaring himself Chief, 'Viciously with full intention he hurled his spear at Ralph', which demonstrates that he has become a violent savage with no conscience about killing an unarmed person.*

Look at the response carefully.

- **Underline** the topic sentence which introduces the main idea.
- **Underline** the short sentence which signals a change in ideas.
- **Circle** any words or phrases that link ideas, such as 'who', 'when', 'implying', 'which', etc.

❹ Read this **paragraph** by another student also commenting on how Jack is presented:

> *Golding gives us a vivid picture of Jack. This can be found when he is first introduced. He describes Jack as 'the boy who controlled' the choir. This gives the impression that Jack is not yet an adult. It suggests he is powerful. The description also tells us he dominates the choir.*

Expert viewpoint: The candidate has understood how the character's nature is revealed in this action. However, the paragraph is rather awkwardly written. It needs improving by linking the sentences with suitable phrases and joining words such as 'where', 'in', 'as well as', 'who', 'suggesting', 'implying'.

Rewrite the **paragraph**, improving the **style**, and also try to add a **concluding sentence** summing up Jack's character.

Start with the same **topic sentence**, but extend it:

Golding immediately creates a strong impression of Jack's character by ... .

....

....

....

....

....

....

....

....

....

....

PROGRESS LOG [tick the correct box]   Needs more work ☐   Getting there ☐   Under control ☐

Spelling, punctuation and grammar

Here are a number of key words you might use when writing in the exam:

Content and structure	Characters and style	Linguistic features
chapter	character	metaphor
scene	role	personification
quotation	protagonist	juxtaposition
sequence	dramatic	dramatic irony
dialogue	savage	repetition
climax	civilised	symbol
development	humorous	foreshadowing
description	sympathetic	euphemism

1 Circle any you might find difficult to spell, and then use the 'Look, Say, Cover, Write, Check' method to learn them. This means: **look** at the word; **say** it out loud; then **cover** it up; **write** it out; uncover and **check** your spelling with the correct version.

2 Create a **mnemonic** for five of your difficult spellings. For example:

tragedy: **t**en **r**eally **a**ngry **g**irls **e**njoyed **d**ancing **y**esterday!

Or …

break the word down: T – RAGE – DY!

a) ....

b) ....

c) ....

d) ....

e) ....

3 Circle any **incorrect spellings** in this paragraph and then rewrite it:

When the boys climbe to the top of Castel Rock the tention builds dramataically as they see sins of the beast and relise they have found it. By the time the chaptr ends Golding ensures that his audiense knows that the boys will never dout the beast's existance again.

....

....

....

....

....

4 **Punctuation** makes your meaning clear.

Here is one response by a student commenting on Golding's choice of the name 'Piggy'. Check for incorrect use of:

- apostrophes
- speech marks for quotations and emphasis
- full stops, commas and capital letters

Since people think of pigs as greedy and fat Golding ensured that readers are reminded of Piggys large size every time they read his name as piggy is also the affectionate name a young child calls a pig it implies that piggy is a likeable character however at the same time Golding ensures that piggy shares his name with the animals the savages hunt and kill so every hunt foreshadows piggys death and emphasises his vulnerability

Rewrite it **correctly** here: ....

....

....

....

....

....

5 It is better to use the **present tense** to describe what is happening in the novel.

Look at these two extracts. Which one uses tenses **consistently** and **accurately**?

Student A: *Golding told us that evil is part of human nature when Simon suggested, 'What I mean is ... Maybe it's only us.' At the time, the boys laugh at this idea, but by the end of the novel Ralph wept because he has discovered 'the darkness of man's heart'.*

Student B: *Golding tells us that evil is part of human nature when Simon suggests, 'What I mean is ... Maybe it's only us.' At the time, the boys laugh at this idea, but by the end of the novel Ralph weeps because he has discovered 'the darkness of man's heart'.*

6 Now look at this further paragraph. Underline or circle all the verb **tenses** first.

Simon saw a vision of the Lord of the Flies, who told him 'I'm part of you. Close, close, close', which confirms Simon's suspicion that evil was not a force outside human beings, but was within them.

Now rewrite it using the **present tense** consistently:

....

....

....

....

....

....

PROGRESS LOG [tick the correct box]	Needs more work ☐	Getting there ☐	Under control ☐

Tackling exam tasks

DECODING QUESTIONS

It is important to be able to identify **key words** in exam tasks and then quickly generate some ideas.

1 Read this task and notice how the **key words** have been underlined.

Question: _In what ways_ does _Jack respond_ to _Ralph during the course of the novel_?

Write about:

- How Jack responds to Ralph <u>both at the start of the novel</u>, and <u>as the plot progresses</u>
- How Golding <u>presents Jack by the way he writes</u>

Now do the same with this task, i.e. underline the key words:

Question: How does Golding present ideas about bullying and the way boys relate to each other in the novel?

Write about:

- Ideas about bullying and the way boys relate to each other
- How Golding presents those ideas

GENERATING IDEAS

2 Now you need to generate ideas quickly. Use the spider-diagram* below and add as many ideas of your own as you can:

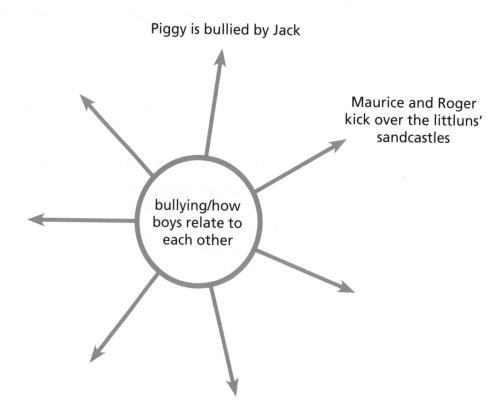

Piggy is bullied by Jack

Maurice and Roger kick over the littluns' sandcastles

bullying/how boys relate to each other

*You can do this as a list if you wish.

PLANNING AN ESSAY

Here is the exam-style task from the previous page:

Question: *How does Golding present ideas about bullying and the way boys relate to each other in the novel?*

Write about:

- Ideas about bullying and how boys relate to each other
- How Golding presents those ideas through the way he writes

3 **Using the ideas you generated,** write a simple **plan** with at least **five key points** (the first two have been done for you). Check back to your spider diagram or the list you made.

a) Jack bullies Piggy because he is physically vulnerable and cleverer than him.

b) Maurice joins in with Roger to destroy the littluns' sandcastles but feels guilty afterwards.

c) ....

d) ....

e) ....

4 Now list **five quotations, one** for each point (the first two have been provided for you):

a) 'able at last to hit someone, stuck his fist into Piggy's stomach'

b) 'Maurice felt the unease of wrongdoing'

c) ....

d) ....

e) ....

5 Now read this task and write a **plan** of your own, including **quotations**, on a separate sheet of paper.

Read from *'What you goin' to do, Ralph? This is jus' talk without deciding. I want my glasses'* (p. 189) to *'I'm going to say – you got to!'* (p. 190).

Question: *How is Piggy depicted in this scene and how does Ralph respond to him?*

PROGRESS LOG [tick the correct box]   Needs more work ☐   Getting there ☐   Under control ☐

Sample answers

OPENING PARAGRAPHS

Here is the task from the previous page:

Question: How does Golding presents ideas about bullying and how boys relate to each other in the novel?

Now look at these two alternative openings to the essay and read the expert viewpoint underneath:

Student A

> *Golding presents ideas about bullying and boys' behaviour in several different ways and circumstances. We see bullying taking place at the beginning of the novel, when Jack is rude to Piggy and later when he hits him. We learn that boys, such as Maurice, may be taught that unkind behaviour is wrong, but the instinct to be cruel, as in Roger's case, can take over if it is allowed to. The effect of being part of a group can turn the boys into bullies too.*

Student B

> *There is a lot of bullying in the novel. Jack bullies Piggy calling him names, hitting him and taking his glasses. Maurice and Roger are mean to the littluns when they destroy their sandcastles. Even the littluns such as Henry become bullies.*

Expert viewpoint 1: This is a clear opening paragraph that outlines some of the types of behaviour and bullying to be discussed. It also suggests that bullying take place in different settings and circumstances. It could be developed further by including the fact that when the boys are together at assemblies, or later as a tribe, they behave like a bullying mob.

Expert viewpoint 2: This opening recounts some of the events where bullying takes place without outlining what is to be discussed in the essay, which is the point of the introduction. Other types of boys' behaviour need to be mentioned.

1 Which comment belongs to which answer? Match the paragraph (A or B) to the expert's feedback (1 or 2).

Student A: .... **Student B:** ....

2 Now it's your turn. Write the opening paragraph to this task on a separate sheet of paper:

Read from *'What you goin' to do, Ralph? This is jus' talk without deciding. I want my glasses'* (p. 189) to *'I'm going to say – you got to!'* (p. 190).

Question: How is Piggy depicted in this scene and how does Ralph respond to him?

Remember:

- Introduce the topic in general terms, perhaps **explaining** or **'unpicking'** the key **words** or **ideas** in the task (such as 'depict').

- Mention the **different possibilities** or ideas that you are going to address.

- Use the **author's name**.

WRITING ABOUT TECHNIQUES

Here are two paragraphs in response to a different task, where the students have focused on the writer's techniques. The task is:

Read from: '"Grab them!" ...' (p. 198) to 'the steady shrill cheering of the tribe behind them' (p. 199).

Question: What techniques does Golding use to show what Jack is like as a leader in this scene?

Student A

> *When the tribe do not obey Jack's order to grab the twins straight away he shouted angrily. 'I said "grab them".' Then they obey. This tells us that Jack leads by frightening people to make them do what he wants. The way Golding makes Jack repeat his words shows readers he is determined to be obeyed which shows how forceful he is and how difficult it is to stand up to him, rather like a school bully.*

Student B

> *Golding describes Jack repeating his command to capture Sam and Eric when he angrily shouts, 'I said "grab them".' Then Golding shows the immediate impact of Jack's dictatorship: the tribe obey. The tribe know they have been told to do something morally wrong, which is why they hesitate. Yet the adverb 'angrily' suggests that just sensing Jack's anger has become enough to frighten and intimidate these boys into choosing to obey him rather than their consciences.*

Expert viewpoint 1: This higher-level response describes the impact Jack's leadership method had on the tribe and on Sam and Eric in the text. It also states the wider implications of his methods and gives evidence. It discusses the writer's techniques, using literary terms to good effect.

Expert viewpoint 2. This mid-level response highlights the effect of Jack's words on the tribe. However, the quotation, though appropriate, is not sufficiently embedded in the sentence. There is one instance of the writer's technique mentioned but no others, and in the final sentence the point made is not developed and no evidence or examples are given.

❸ Which comment belongs to which answer? Match the paragraph (A or B) to the expert's feedback (1 or 2).

Student A: ....   Student B: ....

❹ Now, take another **aspect** of the scene and on a separate sheet of paper write your own **paragraph**. You could **comment** on one of these aspects:

● Jack being able to predict and respond to Ralph's reaction

● How Jack proves to Ralph that he is the boys' leader now

● The way Jack provokes Ralph into fighting him

❺ Now read this **lower-level** response to the following task:

Read from where Jack says *'I've got the conch'* (p. 138) to *'the embarrassment of linking with another's eye'* (p. 139).

Question: How is Jack depicted in this scene and how do the boys respond to him?

Student response

> Jack is trying to lead a rebellion to overthrow Ralph's leadership. Jack is sure the boys will want to get rid of Ralph as their leader so he asks them this quotation, 'Who thinks Ralph oughtn't to be chief?' and 'looked expectantly'.
>
> When the boys are silent, Jack tries again telling them to put up their hands. Even when the boys do not vote, Jack keeps going. This suggests that Jack just doesn't know when to stop.

Expert viewpoint: The quotations in paragraph one are well chosen and give us a sense of Jack's forceful character, but they are not successfully embedded in the sentence, and the word 'quotation' is misused. Nor is there any exploration of what can be inferred from Golding's choice of words. Paragraph two needs a comment on what Golding suggests through the boys' lack of response to Jack. The language is also a little informal at times ('doesn't know when to stop').

Rewrite these two **paragraphs**, improving them by addressing:

- The lack of development of linking of points – no **'zooming in'** on **key words and phrases**
- The lack of **quotations and embedding**
- Unnecessary **repetition**, poor **specialist terms** and use of **vocabulary**

Paragraph 1:

In this scene Golding depicts Jack as trying to ....

which is why he asks ....

implying that this is his view. He believes ....

and looks 'expectantly' for ... .

.... *The adverb* .... *suggests that* ....

....

....

....

....

Paragraph 2:

We infer that Jack is ....

However ....

This recalls ....

....

....

....

....

A FULL-LENGTH RESPONSE

6 Write a full-length response to this exam-style task on a separate sheet of paper. Answer both parts of the question:

Question: *How does Golding explore the importance of civilisation in 'Lord of the Flies'?*

Write about:

- In what ways the boys become uncivilised
- Why civilisation is important in the novel

Remember to do the following:

- Plan **quickly** (no more than 5 minutes) what you intend to write, jotting down **four or five supporting quotations**.
- Refer closely to the **key words** in the question.
- Make sure you comment on **what** the writer does, the **techniques** he uses and the **effect** of those techniques.
- Support your points with **well-chosen quotations** or other evidence.
- Develop your points by **'zooming in'** on particular **words** or **phrases** and explaining their **effect**.
- Be **persuasive** and **convincing** in what you say.
- Check carefully for **spelling, punctuation** and **grammar**.

PROGRESS LOG [tick the correct box]   Needs more work ☐   Getting there ☐   Under control ☐

Further questions   (A01) (A02) (A03) (A04)

1 What do you think Golding intended when he created the beast?

2 Which character do you think has changed most by the end of the novel and why?

3 How does the naval officer respond to Ralph at the end of the novel, and what, given the period in which the story is set, do you think his reaction is likely to be to the events that have taken place?

4 The structure of the story is carefully worked out. What part does the dead parachutist's arrival play in the structure?

5 There are several themes in the novel, such as law and evil. What do you think is the most important theme and why?

6 Every character on the island is male. How might this reflect the period in which the novel is written, and what does it suggest about Golding's ideas about the nature of power and wrongdoing in society?

PROGRESS LOG [tick the correct box]   Needs more work ☐   Getting there ☐   Under control ☐

ANSWERS

NOTE: Answers have been provided for most tasks. Exceptions are 'Practice tasks' and tasks which ask you to write a paragraph or to use your own words or judgement.

PART TWO: PLOT AND ACTION [pp. 8–32]

Chapter 1 [p. 8]

1 a) F; b) T; c) T; d) F; e) T; f) F

2 a) Jack is unkind to Piggy, rudely calling him 'Fatty' and 'flatly' telling him he can't explore. Ralph is kinder, insisting he is called Piggy, 'his name', not Fatty; listens to his advice; and gives him a job to do: counting the boys instead of exploring.

b) The conch symbolises authority, order and civilisation because the boys have to listen to whoever holds it, and it is used to call them to a meeting.

c) Ralph, who calls the meeting, seems calm, pleasant and in charge whereas Jack is arrogant and bullies Piggy. The choir have already experienced Jack's bossy, uncaring style of leadership: marching them in their black cloaks in the hot sunshine. Choosing Ralph might seem like a chance to escape from Jack.

3

Point/detail	Evidence	Effect or explanation
1: Ralph's and Piggy's character flaws and strengths are set up from the beginning.	Ralph climbs quickly and easily, ignoring the needs of Piggy, who is slow and vulnerable-looking, with 'thick spectacles'.	The initially unnamed main characters Golding introduces are allegorical figures who contrast with each other, suggesting they may come into conflict later.
2: The setting seems beautiful but threatening.	'a bird, a vision of red and yellow, flashed upwards with a witch like cry'.	The bird sounds attractive until the mention of 'witch', which suggests supernatural threats on the island, hinting at danger to come and engaging readers.
3: The boys are alone and face the challenge of looking after themselves.	Ralph says. 'Perhaps there aren't any grown-ups anywhere.'	Without the supposedly civilising effect of adults, the boys will rapidly become savages, destroying each other and their world and mirroring what is happening in the outside world.

Chapter 2 [p. 10]

1 a) it is uninhabited; b) he can only be interrupted by Ralph; c) it was shot down in flames; d) he cannot be found after the fire; e) to signal to rescuers where they are.

2 a) Ralph only introduces necessary rules that bring order, whereas Jack wants lots of rules so that people will do things wrong and be punished. This reflects two contrasting approaches to leadership: Jack's dominating, brutal and oppressive dictatorship versus Ralph's democracy in which everyone's views are heard and wise rules prevent chaos.

b) The beast is associated with snakes and darkness, which Golding uses to represent evil.

c) Ralph encourages the boys to see themselves as similar to the characters in popular adventure stories. He tells them his father says there are no unknown islands left so the Queen must have their island on one of her maps.

Point/detail	Evidence	Effect or explanation
1: Piggy's ability to reason and show both insight and foresight could help keep the boys safe.	Piggy points out the danger of fire getting out of control: 'Won't we look funny if the whole island burns up?'	Piggy's words are a warning and foreshadow the fire at the end of the novel when savagery (unreason) takes over.
2: Golding suggests that reason needs to be combined with leadership skills.	Piggy failed to count the littluns because 'They waited for two minutes, then they fell into the sea.'	Piggy has wise ideas but is not respected by the littluns so they will not follow his leadership and do as he asks.
3: The disappearance of the boy with the birthmark shows the consequences of not using reason.	Piggy says 'I don't see him now ...', then 'The crowd was as silent as death.'	The word 'death' suggests that the boy with the birthmark has been killed by the fire: a terrible result of the boys not being sensible.

Chapter 3 [p. 12]

1 Jack is becoming more and more **obsessed** with hunting. He is determined to **kill** a pig. Ralph wants the boys to build huts on the beach so that they have **shelter** and a **home** where they will feel safe because the boys are afraid of the **beast** and having nightmares. He is frustrated because only he and **Simon** are working hard to build the huts. The younger boys just **swim**, eat or play. Jack and Ralph **argue** about which is more important: **hunting** or what is needed for everyone's **wellbeing**. Simon goes off **alone**.

2 a) All the boys are doing whatever they want: for example, Jack hunts and the other boys play, swim or eat. Only Ralph, helped by Simon, seems able to do things for the common good, such as building the shelters, rather than pleasing himself.

b) The boys have nightmares and cry out, suggesting that they are dreaming about the beast. Jack says that when he is hunting he feels as if he is being hunted by something.

c) Simon is associated with the spiritual and mystical in the novel, so he happily spends time alone and at peace, enjoying nature by going off alone into the jungle.

3

Point/detail	Evidence	Effect or explanation
1: Ralph is the leader but Jack is not supporting him.	Ralph says: 'You wouldn't care to help with the shelters, I suppose?'	Jack does not want to follow Ralph's leadership. Later, he rebels and seizes power.
2: The boys disagree over which is more important: building shelters or killing a pig for meat.	'The madness came into his [Jack's] eyes again' and he says: 'We want meat' Ralph argues: 'We need shelters.'	The word 'madness' reveals that Jack is already losing his reason, as meat is not essential since they already have fish. He just desires it. However, the word 'need' shows shelter is vital. Later, Jack's obsession with hunting will lead to murder and make the island uninhabitable.
3: Later, Jack and the boys become savages who kill Simon, then Piggy, and finally, unsuccessfully, hunt Ralph.	When Ralph is being hunted he wonders what the savages will do. 'Kill him? A stick sharpened at both ends.'	The division between Ralph and Jack reveals Golding's belief in the importance of humanity striving to remain civilised. Otherwise human beings' natural desires are destructive and evil.

Chapter 4 [p. 14]

1 a) 6; b) 3; c) 1; d) 5; e) 7; f) 4; g) 2

2 a) Roger is becoming cruel. He destroys three littluns' sandcastles, kicks sand in Percival's eye and throws stones very close to Henry as he plays.

b) Jack paints his face, hunts and kills the pig. He is violent towards Piggy, breaks his promise and lets the fire go out.

c) The glasses are Piggy's personal property. When Jack takes them without asking permission it suggests that the rules civilised society has about respecting people's ownership are being eroded.

Point/detail	Evidence	Effect or explanation
1: Golding presents Piggy as the voice of authority, scolding Jack for breaking his promise and letting them down.	Piggy says, 'You didn't ought to have let that fire go out. You said you'd keep the smoke going.'	Piggy does not speak with correct grammar like Jack or Ralph but he upholds adult, civilised values such as keeping promises.
2: Piggy is vulnerable because Jack does not respect him. Jack hits Piggy breaking his glasses.	Jack was 'able at last to hit someone, stuck his fist into Piggy's stomach', and later he 'smacked Piggy's head'.	Piggy is unpopular and an outsider within the biguns' group, so Jack feels he can hit him. Having broken glasses makes Piggy even more vulnerable because he cannot see clearly.
3: Only Simon and Ralph support Piggy by finding his glasses and criticising Jack's behaviour.	Ralph '... muttered. "That was a dirty trick."'	Piggy cannot look after himself or stop Jack. He is dependent on others to help, which makes him seem even more weak.

Chapter 5 [p 16]

1 a) F; b) T; c) F; d) T; e) F; f) F

2 a) The ellipsis shows Ralph is losing his ability to reason clearly and express his ideas, which a leader needs to be able to do. His own struggle to think helps Ralph realise that although Piggy is physically unfit, the fact that he can think clearly makes him valuable.

b) Firstly, the boys are afraid that the beast is real. Secondly, Ralph is frightened that he will not remain leader and that they will never be rescued. Thirdly, Piggy is afraid that if Ralph stops being leader, Jack will harm him.

c) If the boys do not gather at the assembly place when Ralph blows the conch again he knows he will no longer be their leader, and any hopes of them maintaining civilised behaviour, keeping the fire going or being rescued will be lost.

3

Point/detail	Evidence	Effect or explanation
1: Golding suggests that evil is part of people, rather than something outside them.	Simon is trying to explain 'mankind's essential illness'.	Golding suggests evil is 'essential' – a central part of humanity; and 'illness' suggests evil needs curing. The novel's solutions are the pursuit of reason and choosing civilised behaviour.
2: Golding suggests evil makes the boys lose control and is associated with all that is uncivilised.	Ralph senses 'the breaking up of sanity. Fear, beasts, no general agreement ...'	In the novel, evil expresses itself through the breakdown of society as people lose reason, trust and unity.

| 3: There are no words that can fully explain and describe what evil is like. | Simon tries to explain evil by saying '... maybe it's only us' and 'we could sort of ...', but he runs out of words. | The ellipsis suggests evil is beyond words and cannot be fully described or explained. It is too complex and difficult, perhaps because it is part of us |

Chapter 6 [p. 18]

1 a) war planes are fighting; b) exaggerate when they describe the parachutist and pretend he chased them; c) the biguns to search for the beast; d) Ralph

2 a) The adults are fierce and violent, like the savages. They fight wars against each other without thinking about the impact of their actions on the world they live in.

b) Jack thinks the conch is unnecessary because the boys should be forced to obey their leaders rather than waste time discussing things. This reveals his civilised behaviour is only a thin veneer, and beneath it he is savage and domineering.

c) Ralph successfully appeals to the boys' desire to be rescued and leads the search for the beast, which reveals that he is both braver and wiser than Jack, and has a better understanding of the boys' needs and what they should do to survive.

3

Point/detail	Evidence	Effect or explanation
1: Golding contrasts Jack's and Ralph's attitudes towards taking responsibility for the littluns' welfare.	Jack says, 'Sucks to the littluns,' whereas Ralph says, 'Someone's got to look after them.'	The quotations show Jack as a selfish leader, and Ralph as a caring leader. The contrast in their dialogue suggests that a good leader looks after even the weakest and most vulnerable of his followers.
2: Golding shows that Ralph is able to understand his own and other people's feelings, and have self-control.	'But for the sense of something watching them, Ralph would have shouted at him.'	This shows Ralph understands how fear affects him and others: it leads to unwise choices. He has control over his emotions.
3: Golding shows that Ralph is able to influence others to agree with him.	Ralph points out that 'the beast does not leave tracks. If he did you would have found them.'	As Ralph explains to Jack why they need a different kind of hunt, the boys hear it makes sense and are persuaded to support him rather than Jack.

Chapter 7 [p. 20]

1 The boys are still searching for **the beast**. Ralph notices how **dirty** they have all become and how much more harsh the **landscape** is on the other side of the island. Simon tries to reassure Ralph that he will get **home** safely. Jack discovers the tracks of a wild boar, which they **kill** cruelly. The boys make up a ritual dance to celebrate the hunt and **Robert** gets hurt. When Ralph, Jack and Roger hunt for the beast on the mountain, they find the dead **parachutist** and are so terrified that they flee back down.

2 a) Ralph's memories of a happy, civilised childhood contrast strongly with the frightening, uncivilised situation he finds himself in now, emphasising the difference to readers.

b) The two clues that the boys are becoming savage are, firstly, their unkempt appearances – dirty bodies, long tangled hair, worn clothes; and, secondly, that they make up a primitive tribal song and dance to celebrate the hunt.

c) They are competing for the right to lead by trying to prove who is the best when they hunt the boar, make plans and show courage while searching for the beast.

ANSWERS

3

Point/detail	Evidence	Effect or explanation
1: The dialogue creates an intense, frightening mood.	Jack takes the lead, shouting instructions to the savages circling Robert, such as 'Hold him!' and then later 'Kill him! Kill him!'	These short two-word instructions urge the boys to act increasingly cruelly, violently and immorally, which builds the sense of jeopardy and evil.
2: The chant creates a powerful, threatening atmosphere.	The hunters chant 'Kill the pig! Cut his throat! Kill the pig!'	Each short instruction to be violent has a three-syllable rhythm, giving the boys' chant strength and energy and creating the intense and frightening mood.
3: The verbs in the descriptions reveal characters' strong emotions.	Ralph feels that the 'desire to squeeze and hurt was over-mastering'.	Ralph is a civilised, caring leader, yet the verbs and adverb reveal his shock that even he cannot control his cruel urges. This makes the mood more frightening.

Chapter 8 [p. 22]

1 a) 7; b) 6; c) 2; d) 4; e) 1; f) 5; g) 3

2 a) Piggy comes up with his best ideas, showing that he feels free to think and be creative. He feels such pride that he even collects wood so they can build the new fire. Piggy is so relieved that Jack has gone that he reassures Ralph when they discover the biguns have left too.

b) The biguns enjoy hunting and having meat to eat. They believe Jack can keep them safe from the beast.

c) This is the book's title and refers to the worship of an evil supernatural being by ancient pagan people, and is a name for the devil in Jewish and Christian texts. Simon realises that evil is part of the boys so they cannot get rid of it.

3

Point/detail	Evidence	Effect or explanation
1: Jack is trying to take over as leader because he wants to run things in his own way and be powerful.	Jack says, 'Who thinks Ralph oughtn't be chief?'	Jack is not only jealous and hates Ralph: he is also arrogant, believing that he will be a better chief and that the boys will vote for him.
2: When Jack is rejected he feels so deeply humiliated he cannot stop himself from crying.	'The humiliating tears were running from the corner of each eye.'	Jack is ruled by his emotions, not by reason. The sensible thing would be to accept his position and apologise, but his pride will not let him.
3: Jack's response to losing face shows he is childish but also dangerous.	Jack says, 'I'm not going to play any longer. Not with you.'	Jack's tone is like a sulky and defiant child's, but the words could also threaten, i.e. he will not 'play' but will be deadly serious about taking over as leader.

Chapter 9 [p 24]

1 a) T; b) T; c) F; d) F; e) T; f) F

2 a) Jack makes the feast exciting with lots of meat to eat, and the chance to hunt and pretend to be a tribe. He promises the boys that they will have fun and that his hunters will protect them from the beast.

b) In Lord of the Flies, being part of a group can be fun; it also gives the boys a sense of belonging and a supply of food and water, and makes them feel safe. However, it can also lead them to behave in evil ways because of peer pressure, and a loss of individual conscience and responsibility for their actions.

c) Simon's head is surrounded by light as the 'moonbeam-bodied' creatures gather round it, creating the image of him having a halo, perhaps suggesting that he is a saint or very holy person.

3

Point/detail	Evidence	Effect or explanation
1: Simon can be seen as a prophet-like figure bringing Christ's message about redemption.	Simon is shouting 'something about a dead man on a hill'.	This alludes to Christ's death and the message in the New Testament of the Bible that those who admit their evil nature and actions and want to change will be forgiven.
2: Golding links the hunters with people who rejected Christ and his message.	The savages chant, 'Kill the beast! Cut his throat! Spill his blood!'	The chant alludes to the biblical story of Christ's rejection as evil by the authorities at the time, because he claimed to be God.
3: Killing Simon represents the loss of truth and hope – then evil instincts reign.	'No words, no movements ... but the tearing of teeth and claws.'	'Teeth' and 'claws' creates an image of a vicious beast, representing the evil instincts in the boys which continue after Simon is silenced and dead.

Chapter 10 [p. 26]

1 a) They joined in with killing Simon; b) He forgets what he wants to say; c) the glasses to make fire.

2 a) Jack uses fear and propaganda to control the tribe, such as telling them the beast is not dead, not acknowledging what really happened, i.e. that they killed Simon, creating the myth that they attacked the beast but that it can come back. Jack does not tolerate people disagreeing with him: for example, he ignores Maurice's questions.

b) There are not enough boys, either to carry all the wood needed now that they are further away from the forest, or to watch over the fire to make sure it does not go out. Additionally, the wood is not as dry as it was up on the mountain.

c) During the war trials the Nazis tried to avoid taking responsibility for their crimes in similar ways, for example by blaming the victims, or saying that they were part of a regiment following orders, or lying. Admitting to their guilt was very hard for many Nazis because it would force them to question what kind of people they really were.

3

Point/detail	Evidence	Effect or explanation
1: *At first Ralph faces up to the truth of what they did, and what it means. He is horrified and wants to be rescued.*	*Ralph says, 'I'm frightened. Of us. ... O God I want to go home.'*	*Ralph admits the truth that their evil instincts are terrifying. He is the only person in the novel to call out to God for help, and it appears that his prayer is answered.*
2: *Piggy makes excuses to avoid taking any responsibility*	*Piggy says, 'He was batty. He asked for it ... It was an accident ... I was on the outside.'*	*By calling Simon 'batty' and saying that he 'asked for it', Piggy makes it seem as though Simon was responsible for his own death, while an 'accident' suggests that the murder was not intended. Finally, Piggy tries to pretend he was not really involved in the killing.*
3: *The boys agree to lie to suppress the truth because they cannot bear their guilty feelings.*	*Piggy says, 'We was on the outside. We never done nothing, we never seen nothing.'*	*Repeating 'nothing' suggests how strongly the boys try to rid themselves of their guilt: if they all say they were not involved, then none of them is responsible.*

Chapter 11 [p. 28]

1 *The conch group can no longer make **fire** and decide to confront the **savages** with all their wrongdoing and demand that they return Piggy's **glasses**. The four boys struggle to the savages' **fort** on the rock. Their arguments are jeered at and Jack fights **Ralph**. Roger throws stones at Ralph and then levers a giant rock at Piggy, smashing the conch, the symbol of **law** and **order**, and killing **Piggy**. Jack threatens to kill Ralph too and captures **Sam and Eric**, leaving Ralph alone and running for his life.*

2 a) Piggy asks Ralph to call an assembly, and holds the conch when he wants to speak. He nods 'propitiatingly', reassures Ralph that he is chief and remembers everything, even when it is clear that Ralph is forgetting and becoming confused.

   b) They may be noticing his weaknesses for the first time, because he has just forgotten what to say, and perhaps are aware that he is struggling.

   c) Roger throws the rock straight at Piggy with 'delirious abandonment', knowing that Piggy is blind and cannot defend himself, whereas Jack fights Ralph as an equal. He also takes over torturing the twins to force them to join the savages, saying that Jack's methods are 'not the way'.

3

Point/detail	Evidence	Effect or explanation
1: *The conch group confront the savages over the difference that divides their groups*	*Ralph asks, 'Which is better, law and rescue, or hunting and breaking things up?'*	*This is the choice the boys, representing all humans, must make: between keeping law and order or living divisively and eventually destroying themselves.*

Point/detail	Evidence	Effect or explanation
2: *When Roger murders Piggy it shows the terrible consequences of having no law and order.*	*'The conch exploded into a thousand white fragments and ceased to exist' and Piggy is killed.*	*The conch has symbolised respect for authority, civilisation, and law and order. When it is destroyed, it symbolises that Jack's tribe have rejected all of these values completely.*
3: *Golding suggests that without law and order human beings become worse than animals*	*Roger acts 'with a sense of delirious abandonment'.* *No other animals are shown killing on the island, only humans,*	*The word 'delirious' suggests that Roger is excited to the point of madness, and that lawlessness is an 'abandonment' of all that makes humans good or a higher life form than animals.*

Chapter 12 [p. 30]

1 a) 4; b) 2; c) 5; d) 3; e) 6; f) 1; g) 7

2 a) Ralph reflects on what has happened to Simon; on the smashing of the conch and what it represented – his authority; and on the murder of Piggy. He knows the tribe will become more savage, and that Jack hates him and will never let him survive.

   b) Golding makes the hunt tense by describing it from Ralph's viewpoint, showing several times how he manages to avoid capture before the savages set fire to the forest, at which point readers believe he cannot escape.

   c) The naval officer's arrival represents the restoration of law and order, a return to civilisation, and the end of savagery.

3

Point/detail	Evidence	Effect or explanation
1: *The naval officer wrongly assumes that Ralph's experiences have been like those of a character in a popular adventure book.*	*The naval officer says the boys' experience was 'Like the Coral Island', but 'Ralph looked at him dumbly'.*	*'Coral Island' is an adventure story where shipwrecked boys behave in civilised and heroic ways. Ralph is silent because, in contrast, the behaviour of the boys on the island has been savage.*
2: *Ralph reflects on the deaths, destruction and evil he has experienced while on the island.*	*'the island was scorched up ... Simon was dead and Jack had ...'*	*This lists some of the horrors Ralph has survived. The ellipsis suggests Ralph is traumatised by Jack's evil actions and can hardly speak about them.*
3: *Ralph has realised what human nature is really like, and the value of true friendship.*	*'Ralph wept for the end of innocence, the darkness of man's heart and ... the true, wise friend, Piggy.'*	*Ralph has lost so much while on the island: he is under no illusions about how evil mankind can be, and recognises the importance of civilisation, reason and friendship as represented by Piggy.*

ANSWERS

PART THREE: CHARACTERS [pp. 33–41]

Who's who? [p. 33]

Jack, *Significance*: he is the leader of the savages and is uncivilsed and cruel.

Ralph, *Significance*: he is elected by the boys to lead them.

Piggy, *Significance*: he represents reason and his glasses are used to light fires.

Maurice, *Significance*: he is a key supporter of Jack, but not as cruel as Roger.

Sam and **Eric**, *Significance*: they are biguns who remain loyal to Ralph until captured and tortured by Roger.

Simon, *Significance*: he is a visionary who realises that human nature is evil.

Ralph [p. 34]

1 a) T ; b) F ; c) T ; d) E ; e)T ; f) F

Quality	Evidence	Explanation
Natural leader	*Ralph blows the conch to call together all the other survivors.*	*Ralph demonstrates good leadership skills such as taking charge and thinking of others, not just himself.*
Practical	*Ralph recognises that the boys need to explore to find out if they are on an island (p. 20) and gather the signal fire (p. 37), and he spends days building huts on the beach (p. 51).*	*Ralph thinks ahead and ensures that the boys remain healthy and safe and that rescuers will find them. He sets a good example by working hard himself, rather than just expecting others to do so. Even when the younger boys swim and play rather than complete the huts, he perseveres.*
Sensitive to others' feelings	*After Jack has lost the vote for choosing the leader, Ralph says Jack is still 'in charge' of the choir and can choose whether they will be 'hunters' or an 'army' (p. 19).*	*When Jack loses the election, Ralph realises Jack feels humiliated so he restores Jack's status by suggesting he leads the choir and chooses their role.*
Thinks about how his decisions affect others	*Although Ralph wants to continue the search for the Beast, it is getting late. He decides not to leave Piggy alone in charge of the littluns and sends Simon to join him (p. 128).*	*Ralph considers the likely impact on the others of the decision to continue searching for the beast. He realises they will fear that their leaders have been harmed, and that Piggy is vulnerable, so he sends Simon to explain what is happening and to support Piggy too.*
Courageous	*(pp. 132–5) Ralph is brave when he leads the party to Castle Rock to search for the beast.*	*Even though Ralph is scared, he forces himself to continue the search both because he wants to be a better leader than Jack, and also because he knows finding out if the beast is real is vital for all the boys' welfare.*

Jack [p. 35]

1, 2 savage (p. 66); arrogant (p. 18); powerful (p. 15); bloodthirsty (p. 73); upper-class (p. 17); uncivilised (p. 98); aggressive (p. 75); strong-willed (p. 17); cruel (p. 176).

3 a) F/A; b) A; c) F; d) A; e)F; f) F/A; g) F; h) F

Piggy [p. 36]

Quality	Moments in the story	Quotation
Physically vulnerable	*When Piggy is first introduced he is described as overweight, wearing glasses, and asthmatic. At the end he has to be led up Castle Rock because he cannot see without his glasses.*	'very fat' (p. 2) 'asthma' (p. 3) 'Give me my specs!' (p. 40)
Unpopular	*Jack dislikes Piggy immediately. The boys laugh at his nickname, which suggests that he is unpopular. He is despised by the biguns, partly for his physical appearance but mostly for being lazy and not doing his fair share of the work.*	'You're talking too much … Shut up, Fatty.' (p. 17) '"Oh Piggy!" A storm of laughter arose and even the tiniest child joined in.' (p. 17) 'and a certain disinclination for manual labour' (p. 68) 'an outsider' (p. 68)
Behaves like a parent	*Early on, Piggy sounds like a father scolding the boys when their immature behaviour results in the first fire running out of control, yet later he compassionately helps them explain their fears to the assembly. Before his death, Piggy accompanies Ralph to visit Jack's camp to ask for the glasses to be returned.*	'My! You've made a big heap, haven't you?' (p. 40) 'make sure nothing happens' (p. 163)
Source of reason and wise ideas	*Piggy sees the potential of the conch to summon all the survivors on the island.*	'We can use this to call the others. Have a meeting.' (p. 12)
Perceptive about people	*Piggy tells Ralph that although Jack hates Ralph, he feels unable to hurt him. Instead, he will hurt the person closest to him, Piggy.*	'He hates you too … He can't hurt you: but if you stand out of the way he'd hurt the next thing. And that's me.' (p. 101)
Loyal	*From the moment Ralph is elected until Piggy's death, Piggy supports Ralph's leadership, urging the other boys to give him time to think.*	'You're still Chief.' (p. 172)
Lacks moral courage	*Piggy cannot admit that he took part in killing Simon and tries to excuse their behaviour.*	'It was an accident …' (p. 173)

2 Piggy's glasses represent civilised society's technology and innovation. They are used to light the fires but are broken and then destroyed as savagery takes over.

Simon [p. 37]

1 a) Jack says it, because he thinks Simon faints to get attention and he is unsympathetic, whereas in fact Simon has epilepsy (p. 16).

b) Piggy says it when he and Ralph realise that Simon is missing and may have gone off alone to search the top of the mountain for the beast (p. 145).

c) The beast says this in Simon's vision, prophetically warning him that the other boys' desire for 'fun' will lead them to kill him (p. 159).

d) All the boys chant this when they see Simon coming out of the woods, and, mistaking him for the beast, they murder him (p. 168).

e) Piggy says this to avoid taking moral responsibility for their part in the murder of Simon (p. 173).

2

'However Simon thought of the **beast**, there rose before his inward sight the picture of a human at once **heroic** and **sick**' (p. 112).

'I'm **part** of you? Close, close, **close**! I'm the **reason** why it's no go? Why **things** are what they are?' (p. 158).

Roger and Maurice [p. 38]

1 *Roger enjoys **hurting** others because he is a sadist, which makes him more evil than Jack. In Chapter 1 we learn that he 'kept to himself with **avoidance** and **secrecy** (p. 18). Under Jack's lawless leadership, he unleashes his natural **cruelty**. Firstly, he throws **stones** at an unsuspecting littlun, **Henry**, so that they miss him, but only because he still feels as if **Henry** is under the protection of '**parents** and **school** and **policeman** and the **law**' (p. 65). Later, Roger deliberately kills **Piggy** with a boulder and feels 'a sense of delirious **abandonment**' (p. 200). Roger's role in Jack's group is to be the **torturer**, and the twins tell Ralph that Roger is a '**Terror**' (p. 210) whom they are afraid of. They warn him that Roger has sharpened the stick at both **ends** (p. 211), suggesting that he intends to **impale** Ralph's head as an **offering** to the beast.*

Maurice

a) similar and different; b) similar and different; c) different; d) similar and different; e) similar; f) different

Sam and Eric [p. 39]

1 a) F; b) F; c) T; d) F; e) F; f) T

2 a) they pretend they left the dance early and shudder. b) they are so frightened of Jack and Roger that they feel they have no choice but to join in with the hunt. c) warning him about the hunt, telling him to escape and giving him meat.

3 They reveal how even decent people are corrupted by evil because they cannot stand up against it. However, deep down they still want to do the right thing.

Minor characters [p. 40]

1 Percival, Johnny, Henry, Harry, Bill, Phil, Wilfred.

2 a) *introduces the idea of the beast – a major part of the plot … die (probably during the fire).*

b) *name and address … he has become completely savage.*

c) *hunted and killed, which … Simon … Ralph.*

d) *choose Ralph as their leader … savages willing to hunt him to death.*

3 *The dead parachutist arrives on the island because his plane has been **shot down**. His rotting body is found on three occasions: firstly by **Sam and Eric** who fear he must be the **beast**, an idea confirmed when **Ralph** investigates. Later, Simon realises the **truth** but is killed before he can explain. A **storm** sweeps the parachutist's body out to **sea**.*

4 He expects the boys to have behaved in a civilised way because they are British. He has read books like *Coral Island*, which depicts stranded British schoolboys treating each other decently, organising themselves successfully and enjoying adventures together.

PART FOUR: THEMES, CONTEXTS AND SETTINGS [pp. 42–50]

Themes [pp. 42–5]

1 b) Technology becomes *destroyed or abandoned*. Example(s): *Piggy's glasses which are used to help him see or make fire, and the huts Ralph makes for the boys to sleep in.*

c) Law and order turn to *lawlessness and disorder*. Example(s): *the boys vote for their leader, Ralph, who makes wise rules for their welfare, e.g. hygiene rules, but Jack seizes power, ties up Wilfred and punishes him without any explanation.*

d) Clothes become *dirty and torn, and are abandoned*. Example(s): *Ralph's tattered clothes (p. 82); the savages paint themselves and are nearly naked.*

e) Peace becomes *violence*. Example(s): *at the beginning the boys stay together in one group and hold meetings to discuss and agree how they will live together. Later they argue, kill pigs, split into two groups, kill Simon and then Piggy, and hunt Ralph.*

f) The beautiful tropical island becomes *a charred ruin*. Example(s): *the boys set fire to the vegetation, leaving Ralph with no place to hide at the end of the novel.*

g) Life turns into *death*. Example(s): *the boy with the mulberry birthmark is killed accidentally, then Simon is killed when the boys get carried away in the dance, and finally Piggy is deliberately murdered by Roger.*

2 war, violence, law and order, fear, power, civilisation, reason, human nature

3 Possible answers: the natural world, conflict, loss of innocence

4 Human nature – Golding shows that people are capable of being unselfish, caring for each other and being brave. However, he suggests that we are also capable of evil because we experience the impulse to hurt and destroy others. The novel suggests that society can teach us to control our evil instincts, but without the pressure to do so this part of our nature has the potential to destroy us and others.

Civilisation – Golding suggests that civilisation is passed on by parents, teachers, and institutions such as the police but without their influence it can soon be lost, resulting in savagery. The novel shows that civilisations which have democratically elected leaders, like Ralph, are more likely to care for all the members of the community. In dictatorships, like that of Jack, everything is run to benefit the few who are powerful and the rest of the community suffers.

6 This quotation links to the themes of law and order, and civilisation.

Annotations could include:

'breaking' – ambiguous: it suggests that Jack is doing something wrong and also suggests that rules are like an object that can be smashed and destroyed, as were Piggy's glasses.

'Who cares?' – Jack questions the value of having rules, and why it matters that they are kept when there are no adults to enforce them.

'Ralph' – the elected leader chosen by the boys' vote – he makes fair rules designed to keep the boys safe.

'the rules are all we have got' – having shared rules unites the boys, helps them get along together and keeps them safe.

7 a) Civilisation, law and order. Roger chooses to miss because he is still influenced by a world where parents, teachers and the police stop him from being cruel to other children.

b) Leadership. Ralph is a good leader because he shows courage and is searching for the beast, putting himself at risk, because it will help the rest of the community.

c) Human nature, good and evil. During the conversation Simon realises that the instinct to do evil is inside human beings, not a force outside them. He also realises that people do not want to acknowledge this truth.

d) Civilisation, reason. The glasses are a form of technology that help the boys light a fire, an ability that separates humans from animals. They also symbolise reason because Piggy is intellectual and can 'see' how to solve problems.

e) Civilisation, law and order, reason. It is used to call together the assembly and only the person holding it can speak. When it is smashed this symbolises the end of democracy, law and order, and the rule of reason – a lawless dictatorship based on instinct, led by Jack, takes over.

ANSWERS

Point/detail	Evidence	Effect or explanation
1: Golding suggests that savagery is frightening and unnatural.	'This dreadful eruption from an unknown world made her frantic …'	The pig is an animal but is not used to savage behaviour, suggesting that this behaviour does not occur in nature but only in humans.
2: Savagery is cruel and causes great and unnecessary suffering.	'the terrified squealing became a high-pitched scream.'	Roger searches for a way to make the sow suffer far more than it needs to provide their meal – he tortures her so she screams with all her might.
3: It can become normal behaviour to those who accept it.	'Robert stabilized the thing in a phrase which was received uproariously.'	'Stabilized' means that Robert makes Roger's savagery seem acceptable by encouraging the boys to laugh rather than be horrified.

Contexts [pp. 46-47]

1 a) *Coral Island*; b) a nuclear war happening; c) dictatorship; d) savage; e) instincts, reasoning and morality.

2 a) Golding shows that without civilising influences boys' savage natures soon surface, as Roger's does. At first society's influence makes him choose to miss Henry when throwing stones, but later he ignores it and kills Piggy with the rock. Golding suggests that savage leaders, such as Jack, create societies where atrocities like these are tolerated, and this links to how real-life events such as the Holocaust were able to happen.

b) Golding's novel has a Christian moral framework, which clearly shows that murder and stealing are wrong. Through the characterisation of the boys, he suggests that evil is part of every human being, not a separate idea. Simon is like Christ, wanting to share this truth with the boys, but is rejected and killed for it.

4

Point/detail	Evidence	Effect or explanation
1: Jack is head boy of his school, which makes him arrogant and think that he is entitled to lead.	'"I ought to be chief," said Jack with simple arrogance, "because I'm chapter chorister and head boy. I can sing C sharp."' (p. 18)	We can see the hierarchy and class divisions of 1950s society reflected in the behaviour of boys such as Jack.
2: Jack shows contempt for people who do not share his upbringing.	'Who cares what you believe Fatty.' (p. 97)	The middle classes sometimes failed to respect people from lower classes or to value their contributions.
3: Jack rapidly descends into savagery.	'He was safe from shame or self-consciousness behind the mask of his paint …' (p.154)	Jack's choir robes are an outward sign of civilisation, but this is shown to be superficial and is lost as easily as he is able to change his appearance.

Settings [pp. 48–9]

1 Mountain top – where the signal fire is first lit, but later the boys believe it is where the beast lives, and it is in fact where the parachutist's body lands and is found by Samneric.

Castle Rock – the fort which Jack chooses as the base for his tribe. It is where Roger drops the boulder onto Piggy and kills him, and where the conch is shattered.

The huts – where the boys in Ralph's group sleep.

The pool – where Ralph first swims and the other boys do later.

The platform – where Ralph blows the conch and calls the first assembly. Other assemblies take place here too, so it comes to represent civilised order in contrast to the gatherings of Jack's savages at Castle Rock.

2 a) Castle Rock is a high vantage point but has no water, fruit trees or vegetation to act as shelter. Everything they need to survive has to be carried up onto it.

b) Jack chooses Castle Rock as a base because it is easy to defend, showing that his priorities as a leader are not to look after the boys' needs but to make sure he can fight and win if he has to.

c) The jungle where Jack hunts reflects his untamed human nature. It is wild and terrifying, with 'primitive' nests housing birds who 'shatter' the silence with cries that seem to 'come out of the abyss of ages'. The noun 'abyss' suggests the depths from which sudden reactions, impulses and instincts arise, and as it is also associated with religious ideas of hell and torment, it hints that instincts have evil sources.

d) The sheer power and impressive size of the sea on the other side of the island make other places seem so far away that Ralph feels there is no hope of rescue. When he is on the beach in front of the lagoon (where the boys play and can swim) he can believe the distance is not so great and that they will be rescued.

PART FIVE: FORM, STRUCTURE AND LANGUAGE [p. 51–6]

Form [p. 51]

1 *'Lord of the Flies' is a dystopian novel which draws on several genres. Firstly, it is a boys' **adventure** story, like 'Coral Island', with boys stranded on a desert island.*

*However, it also alludes to the boarding school stories popular in the early **twentieth** century. Golding drew on the comic figure of Billy Bunter in the characterisation of **Piggy**, who is **overweight**, wears **glasses** and is a figure of fun. The novel also works as an allegory, with characters representing **ideas** and the story conveying the message that without **civilisation** savagery takes over.*

2 a) Simon represents Christian spirituality, he brings the truth about human nature's evil and, like Christ, he is rejected and killed for it. He has visions such as that of the Lord of the Flies speaking to him, and prophesies events that will happen such as Ralph being rescued, and Simon being killed by the boys.

b) Ralph represents civilisation: he is brave, resourceful, a natural leader, kind and decent. He follows society's rules, controls his impulses and makes wise decisions.

c) Piggy represents reason and scientific thinking. He can think strategically and values the wisdom of adults.

d) Jack represents savagery and human instinct. He acts on impulse, and is violent and emotional, lacking self-control.

Structure [pp. 52–3]

1 a) 5; b) 3; c) 6; d) 4; e) 2; f) 1

2 a) Piggy's death, which is caused by Roger rolling a boulder at him; b) Ralph being hunted like a pig at the end of the novel; c) Simon's death, which happens when all the boys named play at the feast, chanting the tribal song.

3

Point/detail	Evidence	Effect or explanation
1: *Telling the events in chronological order enables the story to build to a climax.*	*Readers see the deterioration of the relationship between Ralph and Jack, and Jack's increasing savagery.*	*By the end, we have seen the savages' murders of Simon and Piggy, and expect Ralph to be their third victim.*
2: *Golding's* **foreshadowing** *at what may come next creates a sense of threat and menace.*	*The tribe's celebration of pig-hunting becomes more detailed. First Robert (p. 125) and later Robert and Maurice (p. 145) act out the death of the pig.*	*This foreshadows the way the tribe will surround and kill Simon, but also how they will later hunt Ralph as if he is a pig to be slaughtered at the end of the novel.*
3: *Golding creates a sense of* **jeopardy** *as the hunters get closer and closer to Ralph, and the fire means that he cannot escape.*	*'… jagged fringe of menace and was almost overhead' (p. 222)*	*'Menace' is an evil threat – which is what the savages are to Ralph. Here they are 'almost' on top of him. They can't get any closer without actually catching him.*

Language [pp. 54–6]

1 a) consonance; b) onomatopoeia; c) personification; d) repetition; e) metaphor.

2 a) Ralph speaks in grammatically correct standard English, with a little casual schoolboy slang such as 'Sucks to'. He refers to his father as 'father', which was how the middle classes referred to their male parent. In contrast, Piggy's grammar is incorrect, e.g. 'I didn't expect nothing', which should end with 'anything', and the casual phrase 'You can't half', which is more adult. This suggests he is less well educated than Ralph, and spends more time with adults than with other schoolboys. He refers to his parents as his 'mum' and 'dad', which was how working-class people referred to parents.

b) Jack uses abbreviations for place names, such as 'Gib.' and 'Addis', and a vocabulary that only people from a public school or choir would be familiar with, such as 'matins' and 'precentor'. His familiarity with these words suggests that he is part of that world. Additionally, he does not see the need to make his meaning clear to others, suggesting either that he expects them to know, or, arrogantly, that they should make the effort to understand him instead.

3 The phrase 'took up' uses Saxon vocabulary; 'antiphonal' is Latinate. This sentence reflects the twins' inner conflict: behaving like primitive savages; or holding on to the civilised values they were taught at home, and being loyal and reluctant to harm Ralph.

4 a) Dashes are used, rather than conventional punctuation (capital letters and full stops), for these brief, simple statements. This suggests that the speakers are losing their civilised natures, and their ability to communicate and reason clearly. Using expressive punctuation helps to convey Golding's idea that civilisation helps people to get along, and that without it things fall apart.

b) The use of synecdoche reduces Ralph to just a part of him, his 'shock of hair', and Piggy to a 'bag of fat'. It shows how in his savagery Roger no longer sees Ralph and Piggy as fully human and worthy of respect. Synecdoche helps to convey Golding's idea that savagery reduces people's moral awareness and results in people treating other human beings in atrocious ways as if they no longer see them as equals.

3

Point/detail	Evidence	Effect or explanation
1: *Ralph is compared to animals as he is hunted.*	*'He wormed his way …'* *'… like a cat …'*	*In these similes Ralph is compared to small animals. Readers know how brutally the savages kill pigs, larger than cats or worms, so Ralph does not seem to stand a chance.*
2: *Ralph cannot recognise the boys individually; they all appear to be savages.*	*'A smallish savage … a savage striped red and white …'*	*The repetition of 'savage' reminds the reader of the hunters' ferocious instincts. They are no longer civilised individuals with names but a terrifying pack working together against one boy.*
3: *Ralph speaks to himself in formal, civilised language.*	*'If only one had time to think!'*	*'One' reminds us that Ralph is alone, but the speech also points out that he is not instinctive like the savages. He thinks and speaks in complex language. Readers have seen him needing longer and longer to think and make decisions. This makes him seem very vulnerable now.*

PART SIX: PROGRESS BOOSTER [pp. 58–71]

Writing skills [p. 58]

2 **Student A**: Level – Mid

Why? *The student uses quotations to prove the point and makes comments on what they show, but does not develop these ideas fully.*

Student B: Level – High

Why? *The student uses apt quotations to support views, and analyses the text. Student B's comment is developed into an idea about the text.*

3 *The word 'twitched' suggests that Jack cannot control his revulsion on remembering what he has done. This shows that he is not as indifferent as he pretends to be and not as callous as he will be by the end of the novel.*

4, 5, 6

After Jack lets the signal fire go out, Golding shows how his pride affects him when he hits Piggy in the stomach and says, 'You would, would you Fatty?' This **suggests** *that, rather than admit he has done something wrong, Jack bullies Piggy, who is weaker than him and is unlikely to hit him back. Calling him 'Fatty'* **implies** *that Jack wants to humiliate Piggy. Through Jack's question, Golding* **reveals** *that Jack is pretending to defend himself, when really he is bullying Piggy.*

Making inferences and interpretations [pp. 60–1]

1 *During the assembly when the boys discuss the beast, <u>Piggy shows contempt for the idea that it could be a ghost, asking, 'What are we? Humans? Or animals? Or savages?'</u> [He thinks that humans are rational and should not believe in things like ghosts.] His questions also suggests that he thinks humans are a higher form of life: an improvement on both animals and the savages he believes were their ancestors. However, through the novel Golding demonstrates Piggy's error: inside every civilised human being is a savage.*

2 b)

3 *Roger is presented by Golding as the cruellest and least civilised character. At the end of the novel he kills Piggy with a boulder and feels only 'delirious abandonment'. This suggests that Roger has deliberately let go of the civilising influence of the moral code he was taught and is enjoying his freedom. However, as well as suggesting his pleasure, the phrase 'delirious abandonment' implies that he is now amoral, and has lost the capacity to feel civilised emotions such as guilt or empathy when another human being suffers.*

ANSWERS

Writing about context [p. 61]

1 b)

2 a)

3 Golding shows how bullying has an impact on boys by making Piggy physically similar to the overweight, comic outsider, Billy Bunter. When Golding was a schoolteacher in the 1950s the attitude towards bullying was that it was acceptable and victims would become stronger through enduring it. However, on the island boys start by calling Piggy 'Fatty' and 'slug', then Jack hits him and breaks his glasses, and finally Roger kills him. Through this chain of events Golding suggests that if vicious boys are allowed to bully others, their behaviour will deteriorate until decent people like Piggy, the 'wise true friend' Ralph mourns, are destroyed.

Structure and linking of paragraphs [p. 62]

1 Golding presents Simon as a spiritual character. He brings a message about the true nature of the evil the boys fear when he shouts 'something about a dead man on a hill'. The words ['dead man on a hill'] *are an allusion to Christ's death, and in the words of Simon's message Golding links the boys' experience to the Christian view that humans are responsible for their choice to do evil and only God can help them overcome this impulse.*

2 *Golding presents Maurice as still having a conscience. He 'still felt the unease of wrongdoing after kicking the littluns' sandcastles'. The word 'still' suggests that time has passed, and Maurice may have changed in other ways, but he has not yet completely lost his understanding of right and wrong.*

3 Golding presents Jack as a highly civilised boy [who] descends into savagery over the course of the novel. *Initially, Jack appears fully dressed in his choir school uniform, [which] suggests that he is a model public school boy, and boasts that he is 'chapter chorister and head boy', [implying] that he is highly civilised. The [inference] is that he should make an ideal leader.* Later, however, he is a changed person. *Almost naked and daubed with paint, after declaring himself Chief, 'Viciously with full intention he hurled his spear at Ralph', [which] demonstrates that he has become a violent savage with no conscience about killing an unarmed person.*

4 *Golding immediately creates a strong impression of Jack's character by describing how he leads the choir across the sand when we first see them. When Jack is introduced he is described as 'the boy who controlled the choir', which gives the impression that although Jack is not yet an adult he can make a group of boys do whatever he wants. This suggests how psychologically powerful Jack is, and may also hint that his method of leading is to dominate and perhaps use force or threat. Right from the beginning we infer that Jack is strong willed and manipulative.*

Spelling, punctuation and grammar [pp. 64–5]

3 *When the boys* climb *to the top of* Castle *Rock the* tension *builds* dramatically *as they see* signs *of the beast and* realise *they have found it. By the time the* chapter *ends Golding ensures that his* audience *knows that the boys will never* doubt *the beast's* existence *again.*

4 *Since people think of pigs as greedy and fat, Golding ensures that readers are reminded of Piggy's large size every time they read his name. As 'piggy' is also the affectionate name a young child calls a pig, it implies that Piggy is a likeable character. However, at the same time, Golding ensures that Piggy shares his name with the animals the savages hunt and kill, so every hunt foreshadows Piggy's death and emphasises his vulnerability.*

5 B

6 *Simon sees a vision of the Lord of the Flies, who tells him 'I'm part of you. Close, close, close', which confirms Simon's suspicion that evil is not a force outside human beings, but is within them.*

Tackling exam questions [p. 66]

1 How does Golding present ideas about bullying and the way boys relate to each other in the novel?

Write about:

Ideas about bullying and the way boys relate to each other

How Golding presents those ideas

2 Roger enjoys bullying and does it more and more, eventually killing Piggy

Piggy is an outsider and is bullied by Jack

The boys sometimes behave as a mob at assemblies

Even civilised boys become savages when they have to, e.g. the twins

Maurice and Roger kick over the littluns' sandcastles

The older boys' behaviour influences the younger boys' behaviour

3, 4

a) Jack bullies Piggy because he is physically vulnerable and cleverer than him.

'… able at last to hit someone, stuck his fist into Piggy's stomach'

b) Maurice joins in with Roger to destroy the littluns' sandcastles but feels guilty afterwards.

'Maurice felt the unease of wrongdoing'

c) Roger's bullying defines his role in the savage tribe.

'one wielding a nameless authority' (p. 202)

d) Piggy is unpopular because he is physically weaker and lazy.

'fat, and assmar, and specs, and a certain disinclination for manual labour' (p. 68)

e) When they are together the boys behave like a mob.

'The crowd … leapt on the beast, screamed, struck, bit, tore.' (p. 169)

Sample answers [pp. 68–71]

1 Student A: Expert viewpoint 1; Student B: Expert viewpoint 2

3 Student A: Expert Viewpoint 2; Student B: Expert Viewpoint 1

5 *In this scene Golding depicts Jack as trying to lead a rebellion against Ralph's leadership, which is why he asks 'Who thinks Ralph oughtn't to be chief?' implying that this is his view. He believes the other boys are bound to agree, so he looks 'expectantly' for their response. The adverb 'expectantly' suggests that he is convinced the boys will agree with him.*

We infer that Jack is arrogant because he does not realise they do not agree with him but seems to believe the boys have just not understood what they need to do. This is why he tells them 'strongly' to put their 'hands up'. However, they still do not respond, but are silent. As Jack finally realises his defeat, first the blood 'drained' from his cheeks suggesting his shock, but then it returns with a 'painful rush', suggesting the hurt he feels at the boys' rejection of him. This recalls the arrogance Jack showed at the first assembly when he believed he should be leader and was humiliated when the boys did not vote for him then either.